Macmillan McGraw-Hill

Math Connects 2

Chapter 2
Resource Masters

 Macmillan/McGraw-Hill

The McGraw·Hill Companies

 Macmillan/McGraw-Hill

Send all inquiries to:
Macmillan/McGraw-Hill
8787 Orion Place
Columbus, OH 43240-4027

ISBN: 978-0-02-107223-1
MHID: 0-02-107223-X

Chapter 2 Resource Masters

Printed in the United States of America.

4 5 6 7 8 9 10 MAL 16 15 14 13 12 11 10 09

CONTENTS

Teacher's Guide to Using the
Chapter 2 Resource Masters

The *Chapter 2 Resource Masters* includes the core materials needed for Chapter 2. These materials include worksheets, extensions, and assessment options. The answers for these pages appear at the back of this booklet.

All of the materials found in this booklet are included for viewing and printing on the *TeacherWorks Plus* CD-ROM.

Chapter Resources

Graphic Organizer (page 2) This master is a tool designed to assist students with comprehension of grade-level concepts. You can use this graphic organizer in coordination with the appropriate lesson. While the content and layout of these tools vary, their goal is to assist students by providing a visual representation from which they can learn new concepts.

Student Glossary (page 3) This master is a study tool that presents the key vocabulary terms from the chapter. You may suggest that students highlight or star the terms they do not understand. Give this list to students before beginning Lesson 2-1. Remind them to add these pages to their mathematics study notebooks.

Anticipation Guide (page 4) This is a survey designed for use before beginning the chapter. You can use this survey to highlight what students may or may not know about the concepts in the chapter. If feasible, interview students in small groups, asking them the questions in the guide. There is space for recording how well students answer the questions before they complete the chapter. You may find it helpful to interview students a second time, after completing the chapter, to determine their progress.

Games (page 5) A game is provided to reinforce chapter concepts and may be used at appropriate times throughout the chapter.

Resources for Lessons

Reteach Each lesson has an associated Reteach worksheet. In general, the Reteach worksheet focuses on the same lesson content but uses a different approach, learning style, or modality than that used in the Student Edition. The Reteach worksheet closes with computational practice.

Skills Practice The Skills Practice worksheet for each lesson focuses on the computational aspect of the lesson. The Skills Practice worksheet may be helpful in providing additional practice of the skill taught in the lesson. It also contains word problems that cover the skill. Spaces for students' answers are provided on the worksheet.

Homework Practice The Homework Practice worksheet provides an opportunity for additional computational practice. The Homework Practice worksheet includes word problems that address the skill taught in the lesson. Spaces for students' answers are provided on the worksheet.

Problem-Solving Practice The Problem-Solving Practice worksheet presents additional reinforcement in solving word problems that applies both the concepts of the lesson and some review.

Enrich The Enrich worksheet presents activities that extend the concepts of the lesson or offer a historical or multicultural look at the lesson's concepts. Some enrichment materials are designed to widen students' perspectives on the mathematics they are learning.

Resources for Problem-Solving Lessons In recognition of the importance of problem-solving strategies, worksheets for problem-solving lessons follow a slightly different format. For problem-solving lessons, a two-page Reteach worksheet offers a complete model for choosing a strategy. For each Problem-Solving Strategy lesson, Reteach and Skills Practice worksheets offer reinforcement of the strategy taught in the Student Edition lesson. In contrast, the Problem-Solving Investigation worksheets include a model strategy on the Reteach worksheets and provide problems requiring several alternate strategies on the practice worksheets.

Assessment Options

The assessment masters in the *Chapter 2 Resource Masters* offer a wide variety of assessment tools for monitoring progress as well as final assessment.

Individual Progress Checklist This checklist explains the chapter's goals or objectives. Teachers can record whether a student's mastery of each objective is beginning (B), developing (D), or mastered (M). The checklist includes space to record notes to parents as well as other pertinent observations.

Chapter Diagnostic Test This one-page test assesses students' grasp of skills that are needed for success in the chapter.

Chapter Pretest This one-page quick check of the chapter's concepts is useful for determining pacing. Performance on the pretest can help you determine which concepts can be covered quickly and which specific concepts may need additional time.

Mid-Chapter Test This one-page chapter test provides an option to assess the first half of the chapter. It includes both multiple-choice and free-response questions.

Vocabulary Test This one-page test focuses on chapter vocabulary. It is suitable for all students. It includes a list of vocabulary words and questions to assess students' knowledge of the words.

Oral Assessment This two-page test consists of one page for teacher directions and questions and a second page for recording responses. Although this assessment is designed to be used with all students, the interview format focuses on assessing chapter content assimilated by ELL students. The variety of approaches includes solving problems using manipulatives as well as pencil and paper.

Listening Assessment This two-page assessment contains one page for teacher directions and one page for responses/recordings. This assessment, too, is suitable for all students but is designed primarily for use with students who may have difficulty reading test materials. The assessment directions progress in difficulty from simple at the beginning of the year to more extensive at the end of the year.

Chapter Project Rubric This one-page rubric is designed for use in assessing the chapter project. You may want to distribute copies of the rubric when you assign the project and use the rubric to record each student's chapter project score.

Chapter Foldables Rubric This one-page rubric is designed to assess the chapter Foldable. It is written to the students, telling them what you will be looking for as you evaluate their completed Foldable.

Leveled Chapter Tests

- *Form 1* assesses basic chapter concepts through multiple-choice questions and is designed for use with below-level students.

- *Form 2A* is designed for on-level students and is primarily for those who may have missed the Form 1 test. It may be used as a retest for students who received additional instruction following the Form 1 test.

- *Form 2B* is designed for students with a below-level command of the English language.

- *Form 2C* is a free-response test designed for on-level students.

- *Form 2D* is written for students with a below-level command of the English language.

Cumulative Test Practice This two-page test, aimed at on-level students, offers a page of multiple-choice questions and a page of free-response questions.

Answers

The answers for the Anticipation Guide and Lesson Resources are provided as reduced pages with answers appearing in black. Full size line-up answer keys are provided for the Assessment Masters.

Name _____

Graphic Organizer

Word Web

A suggestion for how to complete this graphic organizer can be found in the answer pages at the back of this book.

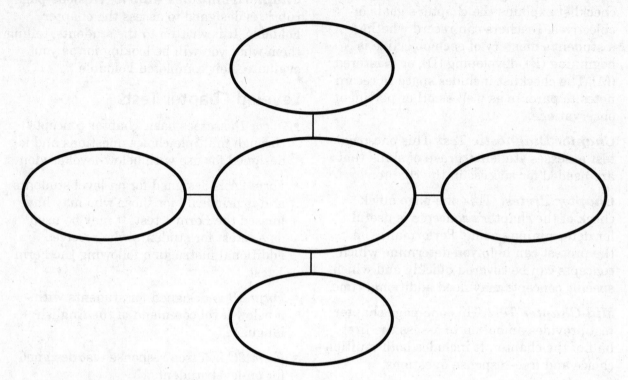

Name _____

Student Glossary

add (addition, adding)	To join together sets to find the total or sum. $2 + 5 = 7$ [Lesson 2-1]
addend	Any numbers or quantities being added together. 2 is an *addend* and 3 is an *addend*. [Lesson 2-1] $2 + 3 = 5$
doubles	Two addends that are the same number $7 + 7 = 14$ [Lesson 2-4]
near doubles	$7 + 8 = \square$ Think of $7 + 7 = 14$ [Lesson 2-5]
sum	The answer to an addition problem. [Lesson 2-1] $2 + 4 = 6$

Name _____

Anticipation Guide

Preparation: Base-ten blocks and counters are needed for this activity.

Directions: Before you begin Chapter 2, distribute these questions to students. Read the questions along with students, giving them time to answer each. You may want to ask the same questions after students complete the chapter.

Before Chapter		After Chapter
	1. What can you say about the sum of 2 + 6 and the sum of 6 + 2? _____	
	2. What are the addends in 4 + 5 = 9? Circle them.	
	3. Which is a doubles fact? $\begin{array}{c} 5 \\ +\,4 \\ \hline 9 \end{array} \qquad \begin{array}{c} 4 \\ +\,4 \\ \hline 8 \end{array} \qquad \begin{array}{c} 3 \\ +\,4 \\ \hline 7 \end{array}$	
	4. 7 + _____ = 7	
	5. Use the number line to solve. 1 2 3 4 5 6 7 8 9 10 11 12 13 14 15 16 17 18 19 20 $12 + 7 = $ _____	
	6. Use a ⬚⬚⬚⬚⬚⬚⬚⬚⬚⬚ or ◉ ◉ to find $7 + 6 = $ _____	
	7. Find the sum. $3 + 7 + 4 = $ _____	
	8. Velma is planting flowers for her mom. She plants 3 tulips on Monday. On Tuesday, she plants 1 daisy. On Wednesday she plants 4 sunflowers. How many flowers did she plant? _____ flowers	

2

Chapter 2 Game

Adding to Move

Ready

You will need:

20 index cards

Marker

2 game pieces

Gameboard

1	2	3	4	5	6	7	8	9	10
11	12	13	14	15	16	17	18	19	20
21	22	23	24	25	26	27	28	29	30
31	32	33	34	35	36	37	38	39	40
41	42	43	44	45	46	47	48	49	50
51	52	53	54	55	56	57	58	59	60
61	62	63	64	65	66	67	68	69	70
71	72	73	74	75	76	77	78	79	80
81	82	83	84	85	86	87	88	89	90
91	92	93	94	95	96	97	98	99	100

Set

Prepare two sets of cards, each numbered 0–9 with one number per card and two cards for each number. Mix each set of cards and place each set facedown. Make a game board like the one shown, or use a hundred chart.

GO!

1. Place both game pieces on 1, Start.

2. Player 1 draws a card from each stack of cards. The player finds the sum of the numbers on the cards he or she has drawn and moves the number of spaces equal to the sum.

3. The player places the cards faceup at the bottom of the stack.

4. Repeat the activity with player 2. Take turns drawing cards.

5. When the cards in the stacks are all faceup, mix them and place them facedown. The game is over when a player reaches 100.

Name _____

Reteach

Addition Properties

$2 + 3 =$ ___5___

$3 + 2 =$ ___5___

The order of the addends is changed. The sum is the same.

$4 + 0 =$ ___4___

$0 + 4 =$ ___4___

Add 0 to a number. The sum is the same as the other addend.

Find each sum.

1.

$8 + 4 =$ ___12___

$4 + 8 =$ ___12___

2.

$5 + 0 =$ _____

$0 + 5 =$ _____

3.

$3 + 4 =$ _____

$4 + 3 =$ _____

4.

$1 + 8 =$ _____

$8 + 1 =$ _____

5.

$5 + 3 =$ _____

$3 + 5 =$ _____

6.

$6 + 5 =$ _____

$5 + 6 =$ _____

6

Name _____

Skills Practice

Addition Properties

Find each sum.

1.   3   2
     $+2$ $+3$
      5

2.   5   7
     $+7$ $+5$

3.   2   0
     $+0$ $+2$

4.   4   5
     $+5$ $+4$

5.   7   0
     $+0$ $+7$

6.   4   2
     $+2$ $+4$

7.   5   6
     $+6$ $+5$

8.   3   4
     $+4$ $+3$

9.   7   4
     $+4$ $+7$

10.   7   2
      $+2$ $+7$

11.   0   3
      $+3$ $+0$

12.   4   6
      $+6$ $+4$

13. $8 + 3 =$ _____

   $3 + 8 =$ _____

14. $6 + 4 =$ _____

   $4 + 6 =$ _____

15. $3 + 9 =$ _____

   $9 + 3 =$ _____

Solve.

16. There are 2 brown frogs.
There are 8 green frogs.

How many frogs are there?

_____ frogs

17. There are 8 spotted turtles.
There are 2 striped turtles.

How many turtles are there?

_____ turtles

Name _____

Homework Practice

Addition Properties

Find each sum.

1.   7   2
   + 2   + 7

2.   3   9
   + 9   + 3

3.   4   9
   + 9   + 4

4.   7   1
   + 1   + 7

5. $7 + 5 =$ _____

   $5 + 7 =$ _____

6. $6 + 2 =$ _____

   $2 + 6 =$ _____

7. $1 + 7 =$ _____

   $7 + 1 =$ _____

8. $5 + 4 =$ _____

   $4 + 5 =$ _____

Solve.

9. The zoo has 4 striped snakes. It has 2 yellow snakes, too.

How many total snakes?

_____ snakes

10. There are 2 brown bears. There are 4 black bears.

How many bears are there?

_____ bears

11. There are 7 blue birds. There are 3 red birds. How many birds are there in all?

_____ birds

2-1

Problem-Solving Practice

Addition Properties

Use what you know about addition properties to solve.

1. What two addition facts can April use to find the total number of dots on this domino?

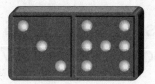

_____ + _____ = _____   _____ + _____ = _____

2. What two addition facts can Ken write to match these base-ten blocks?

_____ + _____ = _____

_____ + _____ = _____

3. Manuel's team scores 8 runs in the first game. They score |||| runs in the second game. Show two ways you can find the total number of runs.

First Game   Second Game

卌 ||| ||||

_____◯_____◯_____   _____◯_____◯_____

4. Cassie knows that $7 + 0 = 7$. How can she use the same addends to write the fact another way?

_____ + _____ = _____

5. Emma knows that $4 + 5 = 9$. How can Emma use the same addends to write the fact another way?

_____ + _____ = _____

2-1

Enrich

Snacking Sums

1. During snack time, Joshua likes to use his snacks to solve math problems.

   He has 7 grapes and 5 pretzel sticks. He chooses the addition sentence 7 + 5 = 12 to describe his snack.

   Which snack does Joshua eat first? _____

   What addition sentence would you write to show that Joshua ate the other snack first? _____

___

2. Devon has 7 apple slices and 7 crackers. She thinks that there is only one addition sentence to describe her snack.

   Do you agree? _____

   Write the addition sentence or sentences. _____

___

3. Rico has 8 carrot sticks and 3 celery sticks. Carrots are his favorite snack. Write an addition sentence to show

   that he ate his favorite snack first. _____

   Write an addition sentence to show another way Rico could eat

   his snack. _____

___

4. On the back of this page or another piece of paper, combine the sums from problems 1, 2, and 3. How many snacks did the students eat?

___

Name _____

Reteach

Count On to Add

You can use squares to count on.

Find 5 + 3. Start at 5. Count on 3.

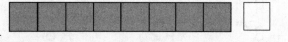

12 3 4 5 6 7 8

$5 + 3 = \underline{8}$

$$\begin{array}{r} 5 \\ +\,3 \\ \hline 8 \end{array}$$

Use the squares. Add squares to count on.

1. $8 + 1 = \underline{9}$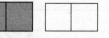

2. $6 + 2 = \underline{}$

3. $7 + 3 = \underline{}$

4. $5 + 1 = \underline{}$

5. $9 + 3 = \underline{}$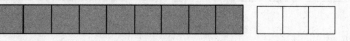

6. $7 + 2 = \underline{}$

7. $6 + 3 = \underline{}$

Chapter Resources

Name _____

Skills Practice

Count On to Add

You can use a number line to add.

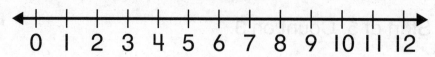

Use the number line. Count on to add.

1. $6 + 1 =$ __7__ $2 + 3 =$ _____ $4 + 3 =$ _____

---

2. $1 + 7 =$ _____ $5 + 2 =$ _____ $6 + 3 =$ _____

---

3. $\begin{array}{r} 3 \\ +9 \\ \hline \end{array}$ $\begin{array}{r} 4 \\ +3 \\ \hline \end{array}$ $\begin{array}{r} 7 \\ +2 \\ \hline \end{array}$ $\begin{array}{r} 1 \\ +6 \\ \hline \end{array}$ $\begin{array}{r} 5 \\ +0 \\ \hline \end{array}$ $\begin{array}{r} 2 \\ +2 \\ \hline \end{array}$

---

4. $\begin{array}{r} 8 \\ +3 \\ \hline \end{array}$ $\begin{array}{r} 2 \\ +3 \\ \hline \end{array}$ $\begin{array}{r} 2 \\ +6 \\ \hline \end{array}$ $\begin{array}{r} 5 \\ +1 \\ \hline \end{array}$ $\begin{array}{r} 6 \\ +3 \\ \hline \end{array}$ $\begin{array}{r} 0 \\ +4 \\ \hline \end{array}$

---

5. $\begin{array}{r} 7 \\ +3 \\ \hline \end{array}$ $\begin{array}{r} 1 \\ +9 \\ \hline \end{array}$ $\begin{array}{r} 8 \\ +0 \\ \hline \end{array}$ $\begin{array}{r} 4 \\ +2 \\ \hline \end{array}$ $\begin{array}{r} 9 \\ +2 \\ \hline \end{array}$ $\begin{array}{r} 3 \\ +7 \\ \hline \end{array}$

Solve.

6. A frog jumps over 6 rocks. Then he jumps over 2 more.

How many rocks does he jump over?

_____ rocks

7. A turtle lays 4 eggs. Then she lays 3 more.

How many eggs does she lay in all?

_____ eggs

Homework Practice

Count On to Add

Use the numbers square.
Count on to add.

1	2	3	4	5
6	7	8	9	10
11	12	13	14	15
16	17	18	19	20
21	22	23	24	25

$$\begin{array}{r} 4 \\ +1 \\ \hline \end{array} \qquad \begin{array}{r} 2 \\ +6 \\ \hline \end{array} \qquad \begin{array}{r} 1 \\ +8 \\ \hline \end{array}$$

1. $\begin{array}{r} 2 \\ +4 \\ \hline \end{array} \qquad \begin{array}{r} 2 \\ +8 \\ \hline \end{array} \qquad \begin{array}{r} 3 \\ +9 \\ \hline \end{array} \qquad \begin{array}{r} 4 \\ +3 \\ \hline \end{array} \qquad \begin{array}{r} 6 \\ +2 \\ \hline \end{array}$

2. $\begin{array}{r} 1 \\ +4 \\ \hline \end{array} \qquad \begin{array}{r} 3 \\ +1 \\ \hline \end{array} \qquad \begin{array}{r} 4 \\ +6 \\ \hline \end{array} \qquad \begin{array}{r} 8 \\ +3 \\ \hline \end{array} \qquad \begin{array}{r} 6 \\ +1 \\ \hline \end{array}$

3. $\begin{array}{r} 3 \\ +3 \\ \hline \end{array} \qquad \begin{array}{r} 1 \\ +6 \\ \hline \end{array} \qquad \begin{array}{r} 4 \\ +2 \\ \hline \end{array} \qquad \begin{array}{r} 8 \\ +1 \\ \hline \end{array} \qquad \begin{array}{r} 6 \\ +3 \\ \hline \end{array}$

4. $8 + 3 =$ _____ $9 + 3 =$ _____ $7 + 1 =$ _____

5. $5 + 2 =$ _____ $6 + 2 =$ _____ $2 + 5 =$ _____

Count on to solve.

6. Ken had 4 fish.
Now Ken has 7 fish.
How many fish did he buy?

_____ fish

7. Cherie has some trading cards. She gets 3 more cards. Now she has 9.
How many cards did she have at the start?

_____ cards

2-2

Problem-Solving Practice

Count On to Add

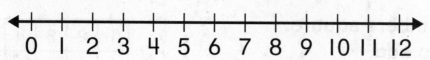

Count on to add.

1. Linda and Nell put their eggs in a basket. There are 6 eggs in all. Nell put in 4 eggs. How many eggs did Linda put in?

   _____ eggs

2. The Brown farm has 2 pigs. There are 5 pigs at the Green farm. How many more pigs do the Greens have?

   _____ pigs

3. Sal's cow gives 3 pails of milk in the morning. She gives 5 pails in the afternoon. How much milk does Sal's cow give in one day?

   _____ pails

4. A farm grows 4 kinds of green cabbage, 3 kinds of tomatoes, and 2 kinds of red cabbage. How many kinds of cabbage do they grow?

   _____ kinds of cabbage

5. Quackers Farm keeps 5 ducks in the front pond. They keep 2 ducks in the back pond. How many ducks are at the farm?

   _____ ducks

6. Peter grows 7 kinds of red peppers. His brother grows 2 kinds of green peppers. How many kinds of peppers do they grow in all?

   _____ kinds of peppers

7. Mr. Rey's fish farm has 5 tanks. He has 4 tanks of baby fish. He also has adult fish. How many tanks of adult fish does he have?

   _____ tanks of adult fish

8. Gus sells 6 bunches of corn. His sister sells 2 bunches of corn. How many bunches of corn did they sell altogether?

   _____ bunches

Name _____

Enrich

Counting Critters

This is an addition square. The sum of the numbers is the same for each row, column, and diagonal. They all equal 15.

First, find the sum of the two numbers in each row. Then use the **count on** strategy to determine the number hidden behind the critter. Write the number in the box at the end of the row.

🐾	3	8	☐
🐾	5	1	☐
2	🐾	6	☐
15	15	15	

Use the number line to count on.

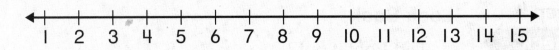

On the back of this page or on another piece of paper, make your own addition square. The sum of each row, column, and diagonal should be 12.

Name _____

Reteach (1)

Problem-Solving Strategy: Act It Out

Jeff likes to watch birds on the way to school. Today, he saw 5 crows and 12 robins. How many birds did Jeff see?

Step 1 **Understand**	**What do I know?** Jeff saw 5 crows. Jeff saw 12 robins. **What do I need to find out?** How many birds did Jeff see?
Step 2 **Plan**	**How will I find how many birds he saw?** I can act it out using _____.
Step 3 **Solve**	**Act it out** I can use red counters to stand for robins. I can use white counters for crows. 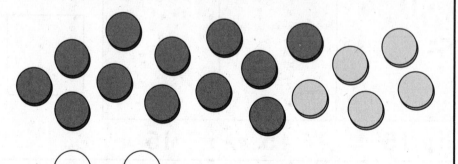
Step 4 **Check**	**Look Back** Did I act it out? _____ Is my answer reasonable? _____

Name_____

Reteach (2)

Problem-Solving Strategy: Act It Out

Solve. Use counters to act it out.

1. Mary sees 1 dog, 4 bees, and 2 swans at the park.

   How many swans does she see?

   _____ swans

   _____

2. 7 cars are in the parking lot. 4 cars leave. 2 more come back.
   How many cars are there now?

   _____ cars

   _____

3. Mia saw 4 bears at the zoo. She saw 9 bears on T.V.

   How many bears did she see in all?

   _____ bears

   _____

4. Kat has 15 balloons. 10 are red. The rest are blue.

   How many blue balloons are there?

   _____ blue balloons

   _____

5. There are 4 markers in the bin. Rick puts 5 more in the bin.

   How many markers are there altogether?

   _____ markers

Name _____

Skills Practice

Problem-Solving Strategy: Act It Out

Solve. Use classroom erasers to act it out.

1. Scott buys all the  and  erasers.

   How many erasers does he buy in all? _____

2. Kelly buys all the  erasers.

   How many erasers does she have? _____

3. Sara buys all the  erasers. Then she buys all the
   erasers.

   How many erasers does she have? _____

4. Ted buys all the  and  erasers. Then he buys 8 more
   erasers.

   How many erasers does he have? _____

2-3

Homework Practice

Problem-Solving Strategy: Act It Out

Solve. Use connecting cubes or tally marks to act it out.

1. There is a number between 26 and 29. It has a 7 in the ones place. What is it?

   _____

2. Randy puts his toy cars in a row. The red car is behind the black car. The black car is behind the yellow car. Which color car is in front?

   _____

3. May has 4 apples and 19 grapes. How many more grapes does she have?

   _____

4. Tom sees 4 ducks. 1 flies away. How many ducks are left?

   _____

5. Betty walked 15 miles. Josh walked 12 miles. How many more miles did Betty walk than Josh?

   _____

6. Ella has 3 dolls: a white doll, a blue doll, and a red doll. The white doll is not the tallest. The blue doll is the shortest. Which doll is the tallest?

   _____

Name _____

Enrich

Missing Information

Ginny's Gems

Ginny collects shiny beads. She keeps them in round boxes and square boxes. All the round boxes have the same number of beads in them. All the square boxes have the same number of beads in them. Look at the clues to find out how many beads are in each box.

⬭ + ⬜ = 14 beads

⬭ + ⬭ = 12 beads

⬭ + ⬜ + ⬜ = 22 beads

How many beads are in each round box? _____

How many beads are in each square box? _____

Look at these boxes. Which set has more beads? How do you know?

Set A

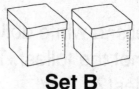

Set B

_____

_____

2-4

Name _____

Reteach

Doubles

Addends that are the same are called doubles.

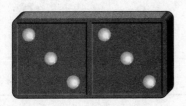

$$3 + 3 = \underline{6}$$

addend addend

Add. Use doubles.

1. $4 + 4 = \underline{8}$

2. $6 + 6 = \underline{}$

---

3. $2 + 2 = \underline{}$

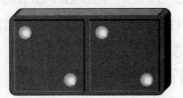

4. $5 + 5 = \underline{}$

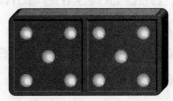

---

5. $7 + 7 = \underline{}$

6. $9 + 9 = \underline{}$

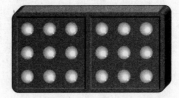

Name _____

Skills Practice

Doubles

Add.

1.

3	5	4	8	9
+ 4	+ 7	+ 4	+ 4	+ 0

2.

3	4	6	8	6
+ 3	+ 9	+ 2	+ 8	+7

3. $8 + 3 =$ _____ $9 + 9 =$ _____ $7 + 6 =$ _____

4. $6 + 6 =$ _____ $7 + 6 =$ _____ $7 + 7 =$ _____

Solve. Write the number sentence.

5. Cameron buys 6 baseball caps. Deb buys the same number of caps. How many caps do they have altogether?

_____ + _____ = _____

6. Andy has 9 shirts. His brother has an equal number of shirts. How many shirts do the boys have in all?

_____ + _____ = _____

7. Circle all of the doubles facts on this page.

Name _____

Homework Practice

Doubles

Add.

1. 7   6   9   8   8
   + 4   + 6   + 3   + 5   + 4
   ___   ___   ___   ___   ___

2. 3   9   7   8   6
   + 7   + 9   + 5   + 8   + 4
   ___   ___   ___   ___   ___

3. 5 + 6 = _____   9 + 0 = _____   7 + 3 = _____

4. 7 + 7 = _____   2 + 6 = _____   3 + 9 = _____

Draw a picture to solve.
Write the number sentence.

5. Kim has 9 pairs of socks. Ron buys the same number of socks.

   How many pairs of socks do they have?

   _____ + _____ = _____

6. There are 7 pairs of twins in the fourth grade this year. How many fourth grade students are twins?

   _____ + _____ = _____

7. Circle all of the doubles facts on this page.

Name _____

Problem-Solving Practice

Doubles

Write the number sentence. Use doubles to solve.

1. Terry cut 8 snowflakes from white paper. Derek cut 8 snowflakes from blue paper.

   How many paper snowflakes did they make?

   _____ + _____ = _____

2. Mr. Bean sells 5 melons to Ed. He sells the same number of melons to Jose.

   How many melons did Mr. Bean sell in all?

   _____ + _____ = _____

3. Carmen has 6 new trading cards. Miguel has an equal number of cards.

   What is the total number of cards they have?

   _____ + _____ = _____

4. Lisa finds 9 markers in her room. She finds an equal number in the kitchen.

   What is the sum of all the markers Lisa found?

   _____ + _____ = _____

5. Mel works at a shoe store. Monday he sold 10 pairs of shoes. 1 pair equals 2 shoes. How many shoes did Mel sell?

   ____ ◯ ____ ◯ ____

6. Paula rides the bus to school for 7 blocks. She also rides the bus home. How many blocks does she ride in 1 day?

   ____ ◯ ____ ◯ ____

7. Claudia is making a rug. It can hold 4 pairs of boots. How many boots will fit on the rug?

   ____ ◯ ____ ◯ ____

8. Dan used 3 stamps. His mom used 3 more. How many stamps did they use in all?

   ____ ◯ ____ ◯ ____

24

Name _____

Enrich

Dinosaur Doubles

Do all numbers have doubles in their fact families?

Color the dinosaurs blue that have doubles in their fact family.
Color the dinosaurs green that do not have doubles in their fact family.

15

20

8

11

14

16

Name _____

Reteach

Near Doubles

Knowing doubles can help you learn other facts.

Think: I know 4 + 4 = 8

Think: I know 4 + 5 is one
more than 4 + 4.
4 + 4 = 8 so 4 + 5 = 9.

4 + 4 = ___8___   4 + 5 = ___9___

Find the sum. Use doubles to help.

1.

4 + 4 = ___8___

4 + 5 = _____

2.

6 + 6 = _____

6 + 5 = _____

3.	5	5
	+ 5	+ 6

4.	8	8
	+ 8	+ 9

5.	6	6
	+ 6	+ 7

6.	8	8
	+ 8	+ 7

7.	10	10
	+ 10	+ 9

8.	7	7
	+ 7	+ 8

Name _____

Skills Practice

Near Doubles

Find the sum. Use near doubles to help.

1. ⬛⬛⬛⬛⬛⬛ 6
    ⬛⬛⬛⬛⬛⬛ + 6

    ⬛⬛⬛⬛⬛⬜ 7
    ⬛⬛⬛⬛⬛⬛ + 6

2. ⬛⬛⬛⬛⬛⬛⬛⬛ 9
    ⬛⬛⬛⬛⬛⬛⬛⬛⬛ + 9

    ⬛⬛⬛⬛⬛⬛⬛⬛⬜ 9
    ⬛⬛⬛⬛⬛⬛⬛⬛ + 8

Find the sum. Use doubles and near doubles to help.

3.

7 + 7 = ____	
one less	one more
7 + 6 = ____	7 + 8 = ____

4.

5 + 5 = ____	
one less	one more
5 + 4 = ____	5 + 6 = ____

5.

6 + 6 = ____	
one less	one more
6 + 5 = ____	6 + 7 = ____

6.

9 + 9 = ____	
one less	one more
9 + 8 = ____	9 + 10 = ____

7. Annie sees 4 bullfrogs at the lake. Zack sees 1 less bullfrog than Annie. Write an addition sentence that tells how many bullfrogs they saw.

____ + ____ = ____ bullfrogs

8. Marcy finds 5 ladybugs. Lee finds 1 more ladybug than Marcy. Write an addition sentence that tells how many ladybugs they found.

____ + ____ = ____ ladybugs

Homework Practice

Near Doubles

Find the sum.

1.
$$\begin{array}{r} 7 \\ + 6 \\ \hline \end{array}\qquad \begin{array}{r} 8 \\ + 9 \\ \hline \end{array}\qquad \begin{array}{r} 6 \\ + 6 \\ \hline \end{array}\qquad \begin{array}{r} 6 \\ + 5 \\ \hline \end{array}$$

2.
$$\begin{array}{r} 7 \\ + 7 \\ \hline \end{array}\qquad \begin{array}{r} 5 \\ + 4 \\ \hline \end{array}\qquad \begin{array}{r} 7 \\ + 8 \\ \hline \end{array}\qquad \begin{array}{r} 9 \\ + 8 \\ \hline \end{array}$$

3. $5 + 7 =$ _____ $9 + 6 =$ _____ $4 + 3 =$ _____

4. $9 + 9 =$ _____ $5 + 6 =$ _____ $8 + 10 =$ _____

Use what you know about near doubles to solve.

5. Look at all the sums above. Circle the **sums** of doubles.

6. Look at the addends above. Draw a box around the addends that are near doubles.

7. Vik gets 8 dollars for pulling weeds. Anya mows the grass and gets a dollar more than Vik. Write an addition sentence that tells how many dollars Vik and Anya get in an hour.

_____ + _____ = _____ dollars

8. Marlene washes 7 pairs of jeans on Tuesday. She washes 1 less pair on Thursday. Write a near double addition sentence to tell the total number of jeans Marlene washes.

_____ + _____ = _____ jeans

2-5

Problem-Solving Practice

Near Doubles

Use what you know about near doubles to solve.

1. Paula knows she can use two different doubles facts to find the sum of 8 + 9. What are they?

_____ + _____ = _____

_____ + _____ = _____

2. Scotty is looking for two different doubles facts that he can use to find the sum of 7 + 6. What are they?

_____ + _____ = _____

_____ + _____ = _____

3. Chris buys 9 boxes of juice for the baseball team. Allen buys I less box than Chris. Write an addition fact to find the total number of boxes Chris and Allen buy.

_____ + _____ = _____

4. One store gives 6 baseball mitts to the team. Another store gives I more mitt than the first. Write an addition fact that tells the total number of mitts.

_____ + _____ = _____

5. Mr. Gomez buys 4 new bats for the team. Mr. Moore buys I more bat than Mr. Gomez. What is the total number of bats they give?

_____ + _____ = _____

6. On Wednesday, the Reed family buys 7 tickets to the game. On Thursday, they buy I more ticket than they did on Wednesday. How many tickets does the Reed family have?

_____ + _____ = _____

7. This year the Tigers made I more goal than they made last year. Last year they made 8 goals. How many goals did they make in both years?

_____ + _____ = _____

Name _____

Enrich

Use Doubles Plus One

Circle the pictures that show doubles plus one.

 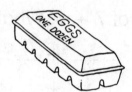

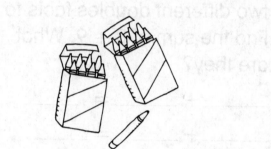

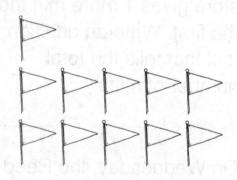

Write number sentences for the pictures you circled.

_____ + _____ + 1 = _____

_____ + _____ + 1 = _____

30

Name _____

Reteach

Make a 10

You can make a 10 to help you add.   **Move 1 to make a 10.**

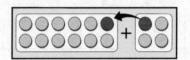

$9 + 4$ $10 + 3$

Now add $10 + 3$.

$$10 + 3 = 13$$
$$9 + 4 = 13$$

Add. Color the counters you use to make a 10.

1.   7   can be changed to $\underline{10}$
   + 6 $\underline{+ 3}$
                                                                 $\underline{}$

2.   8   can be changed to $\underline{10}$
   + 3 $\underline{+ 1}$

3. $6 + 9 =$ _____   _____ $+ 10 =$ _____

4. $8 + 6 =$ _____ $10 +$ _____ $=$ _____

Name _____

Skills Practice

Make a 10

Add. Use connecting cubes to help.

1.

$$\left.\begin{array}{r} 8 \\ + 6 \\ \hline 14 \end{array}\right\}$$ can be changed to

$$\begin{array}{r} 10 \\ + 4 \\ \hline 14 \end{array}$$

2.
$$\begin{array}{r} 7 \\ + 7 \\ \hline \end{array} \qquad \begin{array}{r} 8 \\ + 6 \\ \hline \end{array} \qquad \begin{array}{r} 9 \\ + 4 \\ \hline \end{array} \qquad \begin{array}{r} 9 \\ + 5 \\ \hline \end{array} \qquad \begin{array}{r} 8 \\ + 4 \\ \hline \end{array}$$

3. $7 + 4 =$ _____ $8 + 8 =$ _____ $7 + 8 =$ _____

4. $9 + 7 =$ _____ $6 + 7 =$ _____ $8 + 9 =$ _____

Solve.

5. Ali built 8 model airplanes in October. In November she built 6 model airplanes.

How many airplanes has she built in all?

___8___ + _____   _____.

6. Marty learned to play 7 new songs in January. In February, he learned 5 new songs.

How many songs has he learned in the two months?

_____ + _____   _____

Name _____

Homework Practice

Make a 10

Add. Remember to make a 10 first.

1.
$$\begin{array}{r} 7 \\ +\,4 \\ \hline \end{array} \qquad \begin{array}{r} 4 \\ +\,8 \\ \hline \end{array} \qquad \begin{array}{r} 9 \\ +\,7 \\ \hline \end{array} \qquad \begin{array}{r} 7 \\ +\,6 \\ \hline \end{array} \qquad \begin{array}{r} 2 \\ +\,9 \\ \hline \end{array}$$

2.
$$\begin{array}{r} 3 \\ +\,9 \\ \hline \end{array} \qquad \begin{array}{r} 7 \\ +\,5 \\ \hline \end{array} \qquad \begin{array}{r} 8 \\ +\,8 \\ \hline \end{array} \qquad \begin{array}{r} 9 \\ +\,4 \\ \hline \end{array} \qquad \begin{array}{r} 8 \\ +\,7 \\ \hline \end{array}$$

3. $7 + 7 =$ _____ $4 + 8 =$ _____ $9 + 5 =$ _____

4. $8 + 9 =$ _____ $9 + 7 =$ _____ $6 + 9 =$ _____

5. Look at the addends in the questions above. Circle any addends that you can add using near doubles.

_____

Solve. Remember to first make a 10.

6. Raul wins 8 chess matches on Saturday. He wins 5 matches on Sunday. Complete the two addition sentences to show how many games he won all weekend.

   8 + _____
   10 + _____

7. Carla's team won 6 games last year. This year, her team has won 9 games. Complete the two addition sentences to show how many games her team won both years.

   _____ + 9
   _____ + 10

8. Show how you would explain "Make a 10" to someone who had never heard of it.

Name _____

Problem-Solving Practice

Make a 10

Solve.

1. Mel bakes 6 loaves of bread for the bake sale. His sister bakes 8 loaves.

   How many loaves of bread will they bring to the bake sale?

   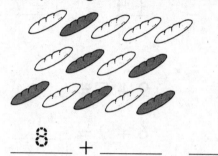

   ___8___ + ___ ___ ___

2. Pauline's mom makes 7 pies for the bake sale. Ann's mom makes 9 pies.

   How many pies will they bring to the bake sale?

   ___ ___ + ___9___ ___ ___

3. Ms. Ling uses part of the money from the bake sale to buy art supplies. She buys 5 boxes of red markers and 8 boxes of blue markers.

   How many boxes of markers did she buy in all?

   _____ boxes of markers

4. Mrs. Quinn buys some pencils. Mr. Lopez buys 7 boxes of pencils. Together they bought 15 boxes.
   How many boxes of pencils did Mrs. Quinn buy?

   _____ boxes of pencils

5. David 's class sent 9 letters to the president. Ann's class also sent letters. The two classes sent 17 letters in all.

   How many letters did Ann's class send?

   _____ letters

6. Mrs. Han's class has 5 fish in their fish tank. Ms. Johnson's class has 9 fish in their tank.

   How many more fish does Ms. Johnson's class have?

   _____ fish

2-6

Enrich

The Top Ten

**Circle 5 combinations of two numbers that equal 10.
Then fill in the blanks to solve the problems.**

```
4   3   2   1   5   9   8
7   4   3   1   9   3   2
6   7   2   1   1   4   5
2   6   6   4   2   1   5
```

1. $16 = 6 + \underline{\hspace{1cm}} + \underline{\hspace{1cm}}$

2. $19 = 9 + \underline{\hspace{1cm}} + \underline{\hspace{1cm}}$

3. $20 = 10 + \underline{\hspace{1cm}} + \underline{\hspace{1cm}}$

4. $14 = 4 + \underline{\hspace{1cm}} + \underline{\hspace{1cm}}$

5. $18 = 8 + \underline{\hspace{1cm}} + \underline{\hspace{1cm}}$

**Now find combinations of three numbers to solve
these problems.**

6. $\underline{\hspace{1cm}} + \underline{\hspace{1cm}} + \underline{\hspace{1cm}} = 17$

7. $\underline{\hspace{1cm}} + \underline{\hspace{1cm}} + \underline{\hspace{1cm}} = 19$

8. $\underline{\hspace{1cm}} + \underline{\hspace{1cm}} + \underline{\hspace{1cm}} = 12$

Name _____

Reteach

Add Three Numbers

You can group addends.
You can use doubles or
make a 10.

Find a double.

```
  4
  3  > 8
+ 4 / + 3
      ----
       11
```

Make a 10.

```
  6
  5  > 10
+ 4 / + 5
      ----
       15
```

**Find a double. Circle addends that make
doubles. Add.**

1.
```
   3                4   4        4   5        3   7        5
   3  [6]           2   4        5            7            5   10
 + 7  + 7         + 2 +         + 4 + 8     + 3 + 6      + 2 + 2
      ----
       13
```

Make a 10. Circle addends that make a 10. Add.

2.
```
   8               4   3        1            8   8        5   6
   2  [10]         3            9   10       7            6   10
 + 4  + 4        + 6 +  10    + 4 + 4      + 3 +  10    + 5 +
      ----
       14
```

Find the sum.

3.
```
   8               8            9            2            8
   3     3         9     8      9    18      7    7       0     0
 + 8   +16       + 1   +10    + 2   + 2    + 8  +10     + 8  +16
```

Name _____

Skills Practice

Add Three Numbers

Find each sum.

1.
3	4	8	4	5	9
2	5	0	3	4	1
+ 3	+ 4	+ 2	+ 4	+ 6	+ 5
8					

2.
4	7	9	8	7	5
8	6	1	3	3	5
+ 2	+ 6	+ 4	+ 8	+ 6	+ 5

3.
4	3	0	2	8	3
6	5	7	4	2	6
+ 8	+ 3	+ 7	+ 8	+ 3	+ 7

4.
6	4	8	5	1	3
5	4	2	3	9	8
+ 6	+ 7	+ 4	+ 5	+ 6	+ 2

Solve.

5. Jan has 4 stamps. Tim has 9 stamps. Ben has 4 stamps. How many total stamps do they have?

_____ stamps

6. There are 4 bear stickers, 6 wolf stickers, and 8 fox stickers. How many stickers are there in all?

_____ stickers

Homework Practice

Add Three Numbers

Find each sum.

1.
$$\begin{array}{r} 6 \\ 5 \\ +4 \\ \hline 15 \end{array} \qquad \begin{array}{r} 6 \\ 2 \\ +8 \\ \hline \end{array} \qquad \begin{array}{r} 3 \\ 3 \\ +9 \\ \hline \end{array} \qquad \begin{array}{r} 7 \\ 4 \\ +3 \\ \hline \end{array} \qquad \begin{array}{r} 6 \\ 4 \\ +5 \\ \hline \end{array}$$

2.
$$\begin{array}{r} 1 \\ 9 \\ +4 \\ \hline \end{array} \qquad \begin{array}{r} 3 \\ 3 \\ +0 \\ \hline \end{array} \qquad \begin{array}{r} 7 \\ 6 \\ +6 \\ \hline \end{array} \qquad \begin{array}{r} 8 \\ 4 \\ +2 \\ \hline \end{array} \qquad \begin{array}{r} 6 \\ 4 \\ +0 \\ \hline \end{array}$$

3.
$$\begin{array}{r} 7 \\ 3 \\ +5 \\ \hline \end{array} \qquad \begin{array}{r} 6 \\ 1 \\ +6 \\ \hline \end{array} \qquad \begin{array}{r} 4 \\ 2 \\ +6 \\ \hline \end{array} \qquad \begin{array}{r} 9 \\ 8 \\ +1 \\ \hline \end{array} \qquad \begin{array}{r} 6 \\ 6 \\ +6 \\ \hline \end{array}$$

4.
$$\begin{array}{r} 7 \\ 3 \\ +3 \\ \hline \end{array} \qquad \begin{array}{r} 6 \\ 1 \\ +6 \\ \hline \end{array} \qquad \begin{array}{r} 8 \\ 4 \\ +2 \\ \hline \end{array} \qquad \begin{array}{r} 7 \\ 8 \\ +2 \\ \hline \end{array} \qquad \begin{array}{r} 7 \\ 6 \\ +3 \\ \hline \end{array}$$

Solve.

5. Benji has 6 fish. TJ has 7 fish and 3 dogs. Max has 4 fish.

   How many fish are there?

   _____ fish

6. The doctor's office has fish tanks. 5 of the fish are guppies. 6 fish are angel fish. 8 fish are mollies. How many fish in all?

   _____ fish

Name _____

Problem-Solving Practice

Add Three Numbers

Complete the number sentence. Find each sum.

1. The zoo has 5 black bears, 5 brown bears, and 2 polar bears. How many bears are at the zoo?

   _____ + _____ + _____ = _____ bears

2. In the baby zoo, 2 cubs are playing, 3 cubs are sleeping, and 3 cubs are eating. How many cubs are at the baby zoo?

   _____ + _____ + _____ = _____ cubs

3. Ellie feeds 3 lambs and 4 goats. Tom feeds 7 ducks. How many animals did they feed in all.

   _____ + _____ + _____ = _____ animals

4. 6 seals are on the high rocks. 4 seals and 3 seagulls are on the low rocks. 5 seals are in the water. How many seals are there in all?

   _____ + _____ + _____ = _____ seals

5. Eric draws 1 lion, 6 birds, 1 tree, 2 houses, and 6 deer. How many animals does he draw altogether?

   _____ + _____ + _____ = _____ animals

6. There are 9 boys, 3 teachers, 2 dogs, and 7 girls watching the water show. How many people are watching the show in all?

   _____ + _____ + _____ = _____ people

Name _____

Enrich

Finish Line

How fast can you add numbers in your head?

Write the subtotals in the squares. See how quickly you can find the sums.

1. $2 + 2 + 1 = $ ☐ $ + 6 = $ _____

2. $1 + 1 + 1 + 7 = $ ☐ $ + 9 = $ _____

3. $3 + 3 + 1 = $ ☐ $ + 8 = $ _____

4. $4 + 1 + 1 + 1 = $ ☐ $ + 10 = $ _____

5. $2 + 8 + 5 = $ ☐ $ + 5 = $ _____

6. $6 + 1 + 1 + 1 + 1 = $ ☐ $ + 4 = $ _____

7. Which answer is the greatest? _____

8. Arrange the answers in order from *least* to *greatest*.

_____ , _____ , _____ , _____ , _____ , _____

Reteach (1)

Problem-Solving Investigation: Choose a Strategy

Jen: It takes me 10 minutes to clean my room.
It takes me 2 minutes to brush my teeth.
It takes me 5 minutes to change my clothes.
How long will it take me to get ready for bed?

Choose a strategy to solve.

Step 1 **Understand**	**What do I know?** First step takes __10__ minutes. Next step takes __2__ minutes. Last step takes __5__ minutes. **What do I need to find?** How much time in all will it take?
Step 2 **Plan**	**How will I find how much time?** I can ____draw a picture____.
Step 3 **Solve**	**Draw a picture.** Step 1 room ЖЖ Step 2 teeth Ж Step 3 change ll It will take me _____ minutes.
Step 4 **Check**	Did I draw a picture showing three parts? _____ Is my answer reasonable? _____

Name _____

Reteach (2)

Problem-Solving Investigation: Choose a Strategy

Choose a strategy and solve.

Problem-Solving Strategies
Use logical reasoning
Act it out
Draw a picture

1. Candy, Dennis, and Serena are trading CDs. Candy gives 6 CDs to Serena and 5 CDs to Dennis. She has 6 CDs left over. How many CDs did she start with?

    _____ CDs

Show your work here.

2. Keith has 4 drums. Shawn has the same number of drums. How many drums do they have in all?

    _____ drums

3. The band practices 6 hours a week. There was a 3-hour practice on Monday. How many hours are left to practice this week?

    _____ hours

2-8

Skills Practice

Problem-Solving Investigation: Choose a Strategy

Choose a strategy and solve.

Problem-Solving Strategies
Draw a picture
Use logical reasoning
Act it out

Show your work here.

1. Mrs. Adler washes 4 sweaters on Monday. On Tuesday, Mr. Adler washes 1 less sweater. How many sweaters have the Adlers washed in all?

   _____ sweaters

2. Ken has 2 blue shirts, 3 white shirts, and 7 striped shirts. How many total shirts does he have?

   _____ shirts

3. Linda is sewing beads onto her favorite hat. She uses 4 silver beads, 4 clear beads, and 6 gold beads. How many beads in all does Linda use?

   _____ beads

Name _____

Homework Practice

Problem-Solving Investigation: Choose a Strategy

Choose a strategy and solve.

Problem-Solving Strategies
Draw a picture
Use logical reasoning
Act it out

I. Tracy read 4 books about lions. Greg read 2 books on tigers. Buster read 6 books on bears. How many books did the three friends read in all?

Show your work here.

_____ books

2. Last month Larry got 3 math games. This month he got 8 spelling games. Next month he plans to get 2 reading games. How many games will Larry have at the end of next month?

_____ games

3. After school, Ms. Blaine put 8 books on the top shelf. She put 2 books on the middle shelf and 8 books on the bottom shelf. How many books did Ms. Blaine put on the shelves?

_____ books

Name _____

Enrich

Lost Numbers

Where do these numbers belong?
Use the numbers to fill in the boxes.
Use each number only once for each problem.

1. Where do these numbers belong? 5 4 2

```
  7             □
              − □
− 3          ──────
─────           3
  □
```

2. Where do these numbers belong? 6 9 7

```
  □             □
− 4           − 1
─────        ──────
  5             □
```

3. Where do these numbers belong? 1 0 8

```
  7             □
  □           − □
− □          ──────
─────           8
  6
```

4. Where do these numbers belong? 3 8 1

```
  □             5
            − □
− 7          ──────
─────           2
  □
```

2

Individual Progress Checklist

Learning Mastery			Lesson	Lesson Goal	Comments
B	**D**	**M**			
			2-1	Use the commutative and zero properties to find sums.	
			2-2	Count on to add two whole numbers up to 3 digits long.	
			2-3	Make precise calculations and check results from the context of the problem.	
			2-4	Use doubles to find the sum of two whole numbers up to three-digits long.	
			2-5	Use doubles plus one to find the sum of two whole numbers up to three-digits long.	
			2-6	Use make 10 to find the sum of two whole numbers up to three-digits long.	
			2-7	Use the commutative and associative rules to find sums of three numbers.	
			2-8	Choose a strategy to solve problems.	

B = Beginning; **D** = Developing; **M** = Mastered

Note to Parents

_____

_____

_____

_____

46

Name _____

Chapter Diagnostic Test

Are You Ready for Chapter 2?

Write the number.

1. 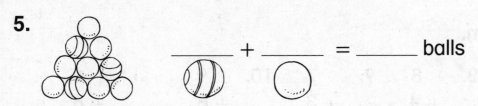 _____

2. _____

Add.

3. _____
   2   3   = _____ erasers

4. _____
   3   5   = _____ balls

Write the number of each group. Add.

5. _____ + _____ = _____ balls

Add to solve.

6. There are 4 ducks in the sand and 5 ducks on the lake. How many ducks are there in all?

_____ ducks

Name _____

Chapter Pretest

Find each sum.

1.
   4   3
   + 3   + 4

2.
   7   2
   + 2   + 7

Use the number line to solve. Circle the correct answer.

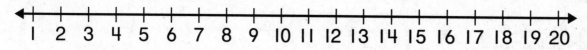

1 2 3 4 5 6 7 8 9 10 11 12 13 14 15 16 17 18 19 20

3. $11 + 7 =$

   17   18   19   27

Add. Circle the doubles facts.

4.
   4
   + 0

5.
   4
   + 4

6.
   7
   + 7

Find each sum.

7.
   4
   + 5

8.
   8
   + 4

9.
   7
   + 3

10.
   9
   + 8

11.
   6
   + 6

Solve.

12. There are 3 cows, 7 goats, 1 tractor, and 2 horses in the Adams' family barn. How many animals are in the barn?

   _____ animals

Name _____

Mid-Chapter Test

Find each sum.

1.   5   3   2.   7   8
    + 3   + 5   + 8   + 7

Use the number line. Count on to add. Circle the answer.

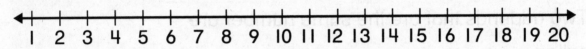

1 2 3 4 5 6 7 8 9 10 11 12 13 14 15 16 17 18 19 20

3. 12 + 6 =   **4.** 11 + 8 =

13   19   17   18   11   18   19   18

Add. Circle the doubles facts.

5.   4   6.   8   7.   6   8.   9
    + 6   + 4   + 6   + 0

9.   9   10.   1   11.   5   12.   7
    + 9   + 6   + 4   + 7

Solve.

13. Amy buys 7 peaches. Lisa buys 1 more than Amy. How many peaches do they buy in all?

_____ peaches

2 Vocabulary Test

Use the words in the box.
Write the correct word(s) on the blank.

| doubles |
| addends |
| sum |
| make a 10 |

1. In the number sentence $4 + 5 = 9$, the numbers 4 and 5 are the

   _____.

2. When you add numbers you find the _____.

3. Two addends that are the same number are called _____.

4. One strategy for finding a sum is called _____.

Circle the correct example.

5. doubles plus 1

   $6 + 6$ $5 + 7$ $7 + 8$

6. changing order of addends

   $7 + 0 = 7$ $5 + 9 = 14$ $4 + 4 = 8$
   $8 + 0 = 8$ $9 + 5 = 14$ $6 + 6 = 12$

7. counting on

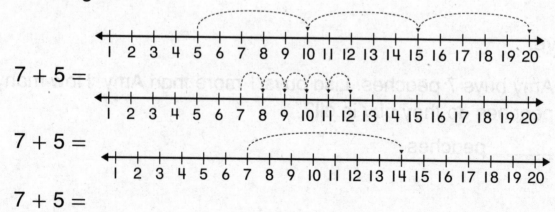

   $7 + 5 =$

   $7 + 5 =$

   $7 + 5 =$

2

Oral Assessment

Preparation: Base-ten blocks, at least 50 ones cubes, and counters are needed for this assessment. For questions 1–5, write the following addition facts on the board or on index cards, one fact to a card.

$$5 + 5 = 10 \qquad 6 + 4 = 10 \qquad 4 + 6 = 10 \qquad 8 + 2 = 10.$$

Directions: This test targets those students who have developing verbal skills—both oral and written. Ask the questions below and have students record their answers, or record the answers they supply.

1. Have students use ones cubes and base-ten blocks to represent each of the addition facts. Have students keep the models for use in questions 2–5.

2. Using the model addition facts, have students identify the addition fact that contains doubles.

3. Ask, *Which two addition facts have the same addends? What do these addition facts show?*

4. Ask, *Which addition fact can help you find the sum of 5 + 6? How does it help?*

5. Ask, *Which addition fact can help you find the sum of 8 + 7 + 2? How does it help?*

6. Have students use a number line to show how to find 8 + 4 by counting on.

7. Ask students to model and then to solve the following problem.

   Karl picks one basket of apples. His brother Earl picks four baskets. Their oldest brother, Frank, picks eight baskets. How many baskets of apples did the brothers pick in all?

Notes and comments

_____

_____

Name _____

Oral Assessment Response Sheet

1. $5 + 5 = 10$ $6 + 4 = 10$ $4 + 6 = 10$ $8 + 2 = 10$

2. _____

3. _____
_____

4. _____
_____

5. _____
_____

6.

```
<──┼──┼──┼──┼──┼──┼──┼──┼──┼──┼──┼──┼──┼──┼──┼──┼──┼──┼──┼──┼──>
   1  2  3  4  5  6  7  8  9  10 11 12 13 14 15 16 17 18 19 20
```

7. ____ baskets

Name _____

Listening Assessment

Preparation: Base-ten blocks and at least fifty ones cubes
and counters are needed for this assessment.

Directions: Ask students to complete each of the following groups of tasks.

1. Use ones cubes to show the number sentence $3 + 7 = 10$.
   Use ones cubes to show the same number sentence with the
   addends in a different order.
   Explain why the sum is the same for each number sentence.

2. Use base-ten blocks and ones cubes to show $7 + 7 = 14$.
   Give the name used to describe addends that are the same number.
   Use base-ten blocks and ones cubes to show how $7 + 7 = 14$
   can help you find the sum of $7 + 8$.
   Write a statement that tells which is greater, $7 + 7$ or $7 + 8$.
   Use the symbol ">."

3. Use counters to show 8.
   Use counters to show 6.
   Use the models you've just made and the make a 10 strategy
   to find the sum of $8 + 6$.
   Write the sum of $8 + 6$ in digits and as a number word.

4. Draw a number line that shows numbers from 1 to 20.
   Use a crayon to show how to find the sum of $9 + 5$ by counting on.
   Write a problem that has three addends, including 9 and 5.
   Use base-ten blocks and ones cubes to model your problem.

Notes

_____

_____

_____

_____

2

Listening Assessment Response Sheet

Show your model here

1. _____

_____

_____

_____

2. _____

_____

_____

_____

_____

3. _____

_____

_____

_____

4. Draw your number line here.

Name _____

Chapter Project Rubric

Score	Explanation
3	Student created an addition game that successfully taught chapter concepts. Student's game covered a broad area of chapter topics and included relevant chapter vocabulary. Student showed teamwork and creativity in designing and implementing ideas for the game.
2	Student created an addition game that successfully taught chapter concepts. Student's game covered a broad area of chapter topics and included relevant chapter vocabulary.
1	Student created an addition game that taught some chapter concepts and included some relevant vocabulary.
0	Student did not accomplish the task sufficiently; the game did not impart chapter concepts.

Name _____

Chapter Foldables Rubric

Score	Explanation
3	Student successfully made, labeled, and used the Foldables to record addition strategies. Student demonstrated and explained different ways to find a sum, including adding on, using doubles, using doubles plus 1, and make 10.
2	Student successfully made, labeled, and used the Foldables to record addition strategies. Student correctly identified some ways to find a sum.
1	Student made, labeled, and used the Foldables to record addition strategies. Student correctly identified some ways to find a sum.
0	Student did not construct the Foldables correctly. Student was unable to demonstrate strategies to find a sum.

Read each question carefully.
Fill in the circle for the correct answer.

1. $9 + 2 = \square$

   ○ 99

   ○ 92

   ○ 29

   ○ 11

2. Which is another way to write $6 + 7 = 13$?

   ○ $6 + 6 = 12$

   ○ $7 + 6 = 13$

   ○ $7 + 7 = 14$

   ○ $10 + 4 = 14$

3. $9 + 0 = \square$

   ○ 0

   ○ 9

   ○ 10

   ○ 90

4. $6 + 3 = \square$

   ○ 3

   ○ 6

   ○ 9

   ○ 63

5. Which addition fact is shown?

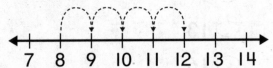

   ○ $7 + 7 = 14$

   ○ $8 + 1 = 12$

   ○ $8 + 6 = 14$

   ○ $8 + 4 = 12$

6. What doubles fact can help you find the sum of $5 + 6$?

   ○ $2 + 2 = 4$

   ○ $5 + 5 = 10$

   ○ $6 + 5 = 11$

   ○ $7 + 7 = 14$

GO ON

7. There are 8 cows in the field. There are 2 fewer cows in the barn. Which number sentence tells how many cows there are in all?

○ $8 - 2 = 6$

○ $8 + 2 = 10$

○ $8 + 6 = 14$

○ $8 + 8 = 16$

8. Which addition fact can help you find the sum $9 + 6$?

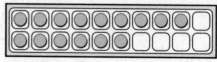

○ $10 + 6 = 16$

○ $10 + 9 = 19$

○ $10 + 5 = 15$

○ $10 + 1 = 11$

9. Find the sum.

$$\begin{array}{r} 7 \\ 3 \\ +5 \\ \hline \end{array}$$

○ 8

○ 10

○ 15

○ 17

10. Add. $4 + 9 + 7 =$ ☐

○ 11

○ 13

○ 16

○ 20

STOP

Chapter Test, Form 2A

**Read each question carefully.
Fill in the circle for the correct answer.**

1. $8 + 4 = \square$

   ○ 84
   ○ 48
   ○ 14
   ○ 12

2. Which is another way to write this fact?

   $9 + 3 = 12$

   ○ $4 + 9 = 13$
   ○ $3 + 9 = 12$
   ○ $9 + 4 = 13$
   ○ $3 + 3 = 6$

3. $4 + 0 = \square$

   ○ 10
   ○ 9
   ○ 4
   ○ 0

4. $5 + 4 = \square$

   ○ 54
   ○ 9
   ○ 5
   ○ 4

5. Which addition fact is shown?

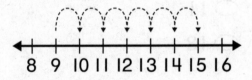

   ○ $9 + 9 = 18$
   ○ $8 + 8 = 16$
   ○ $9 + 6 = 15$
   ○ $8 + 6 = 14$

6. What doubles fact can help you find the sum of $8 + 9$?

   ○ $8 + 8 = 16$
   ○ $7 + 8 = 15$
   ○ $7 + 7 = 14$
   ○ $2 + 2 = 4$

7. There are 9 pigs in the pen. There are 3 fewer pigs in the barn. Which number sentence tells how many pigs there are in all?

○ $9 + 9 = 18$

○ $9 + 6 = 15$

○ $8 + 3 = 11$

○ $9 - 3 = 6$

8. Which addition fact can help you find the sum $8 + 7$?

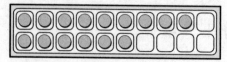

○ $10 + 8 = 18$

○ $10 + 7 = 17$

○ $10 + 5 = 15$

○ $10 + 1 = 11$

9. Find the sum.

$$\begin{array}{r} 8 \\ 7 \\ +2 \\ \hline \end{array}$$

○ 18

○ 17

○ 10

○ 12

10. Add. $7 + 6 + 5 = \boxed{}$

○ 19

○ 18

○ 11

○ 13

STOP

Read each question carefully.
Fill in the circle for the correct answer.

1. $3 + 4 = \square$

   ○ 34
   ○ 43
   ○ 7

2. Which number sentence has the same sum as $5 + 3$?

   ○ $8 + 5$
   ○ $8 + 3$
   ○ $3 + 5$

3. $5 + 0 = \square$

   ○ 50
   ○ 5
   ○ 0

4. $6 + 3 = \square$

   ○ 63
   ○ 9
   ○ 6

5. Use the number line.
   Find $9 + 6$.

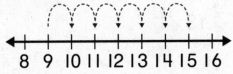

   8 9 10 11 12 13 14 15 16

   ○ 16
   ○ 15
   ○ 12

6. $8 + 9$ is one more than $8 + \square$?

   ○ 8
   ○ 7
   ○ 9

7. There are 9 pigs in the pen. There are 6 pigs in the barn. Which number sentence tells how many pigs there are in all?

○ $9 + 9 = 18$

○ $9 + 6 = 15$

○ $9 - 6 = 3$

8. Find $8 + 7$.

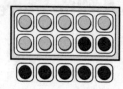

○ 18

○ 17

○ 15

9. Find the sum.

$$\begin{array}{r} 2 \\ 6 \\ +3 \\ \hline \end{array}$$

○ 11

○ 9

○ 8

10. Find $7 + 6 + 5$.

○ 19

○ 18

○ 13

STOP

Name _____

Chapter Test, Form 2C

Read each question carefully.
Write your answer.

1. Find the sum.

$$\begin{array}{r} 8 \\ +\,4 \\ \hline \end{array}$$

2. Add.

$4 + 0 =$ _____

3. $6 + 8 =$

4. Write the addition fact
$9 + 3 = 12$ a different way.

_____

5. Which addition fact is shown?

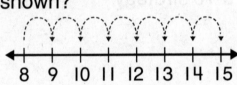

_____

6. Find $9 + 7$.

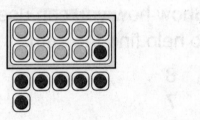

_____

_____

_____

_____

GO ON

7. What doubles fact can help you find the sum of 8 + 9?
Tell why.

_____

_____

8. There are 4 chicks in the yard.
There are 5 more chicks in the
coop than there are in the yard.
Write a number sentence that tells
how many chicks there are in all.

_____

9. Show how you can use the *make a 10* strategy
to help find the sum.

$$
\begin{array}{r}
8 \\
7 \\
+2 \\
\hline
\end{array}
$$

_____

_____

10. Liza sold pies at a bake sale. She sold 7 pies to Joe. She sold
4 pies to Patty and 3 to Tom. Write a number sentence that
tells how many pies she sold in all.

_____

STOP

2

Chapter Test, Form 2D

**Read each question carefully.
Write your answer.**

1. Add.

$$\begin{array}{r} 9 \\ +5 \\ \hline \end{array}$$

2. Find the sum.

$$\begin{array}{r} 8 \\ +0 \\ \hline \end{array}$$

3. Add.

$$\begin{array}{r} 6 \\ +4 \\ \hline \end{array}$$

4. Show another way to write this same fact.

$9 + 3 = 12$

_____

5. Use the number line.
Find $6 + 7$.

```
<---+--+--+--+--+--+--+--+--+--+--+--->
    5  6  7  8  9  10 11 12 13 14 15
```

$6 + 7 =$ _____

6. Find $8 + 4$.

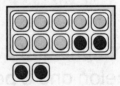

$8 + 4 =$ _____

Name _____

7. Add.

$8 + 9 =$ _____

8. There are 5 horses in the field. There are 3 more horses in the barn than there are in the field. How many horses in all?

_____ horses

9. Find the sum.

$$\begin{array}{r} 8 \\ 3 \\ +2 \\ \hline \end{array}$$

10. Leo buys 4 melons and 8 ears of corn at the farmer's market. He buys 1 melon and 3 peppers from the grocery store and 2 melons from a fruit stand. How many melons does he buy in all?

_____ melons

STOP

Cumulative Test Practice Chapters 1-2

Name _____

Read each question carefully.
Fill in the circle for the correct answer.

I. How many tens and ones are shown?

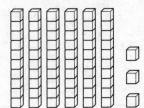

○ 6 ones 3 tens

○ 63 ones

○ 63 tens

○ 6 tens 3 ones

2. What is the value of the 7 in 78?

○ 7

○ 70

○ 78

○ 80

3. Find the sum. $6 + 7 = $ ☐

○ 12

○ 13

○ 14

○ 67

4. Add. $8 + 2 = $ ☐

○ 2

○ 4

○ 6

○ 10

5. $9 + 7 = $ ☐

○ 10

○ 11

○ 16

○ 17

GO ON

Cumulative Test Practice (continued)

Read each question carefully.

Write your answer on the line.

6. Vera bought 6 ears of corn.
   Sal bought 2 ears of corn.
   How many ears of corn do they have now?

   _____ ears of corn

7. There are 10 cherries in the
   bowl. About how many cherries
   would it take to fill the bowl?

   _____ cherries

8. Kayla plants three kinds of peppers. She plants 3 red peppers,
   7 green peppers, and 5 hot peppers. Write a number sentence
   that tells how many peppers she plants in all.

   _____

9. Derrick buys 6 apples. Edgar buys 2 fewer apples than Derrick.
   How many total apples did they buy?

   _____ apples

10. Mimi uses her calculator to add 3 to numbers. She adds in this
    order: $2 + 3 = 5$, $3 + 3 = 6$, $4 + 3 = 7$, and $5 + 3 = 8$.
    If she continues the pattern, what will be the next number

    sentence? _____

STOP

Answers (Graphic Organizer and Anticipation Guide)

2

Name _____

Anticipation Guide

Preparation: Base-ten blocks and counters are needed for this activity.

Directions: Before you begin Chapter 2, distribute these questions to students. Read the questions along with students, giving them time to answer each. You may want to ask the same questions after students complete the chapter.

Before Chapter		After Chapter
	1. What can you say about the sum of 2 + 6 and the sum of 6 + 2? _____	The sums are the same.
	2. What are the addends in ④ + ⑤ = 9? Circle them.	0
	3. Which is a doubles fact? $\begin{array}{r}5\\+4\\\hline9\end{array}$ $\begin{array}{r}4\\+4\\\hline8\end{array}$ $\begin{array}{r}3\\+4\\\hline7\end{array}$	7
	4. 7 + ___ = 7	19
	5. Use the number line to solve. ←1 2 3 4 5 6 7 8 9 10 11 12 13 14 15 16 17 18 19 20→ 12 + 7 = ___	
	6. Use a ▭▭▭ or ● to find	13
	7 + 6 = ___	
	7. Find the sum. 3 + 7 + 4 = ___	14
	8. Velma is planting flowers for her mom. She plants 3 tulips on Monday. On Tuesday, she plants 1 daisy. On Wednesday she plants 4 sunflowers. How many flowers did she plant? ___ flowers	8

Answers

2

Name _____

Graphic Organizer

Word Web

A suggestion for how to complete this graphic organizer can be found in the answer pages at the back of this book.

near doubles

doubles

add

make ten

count on

Note to Teacher: A word web can help students learn and understand multiple strategies. Write the word *add* in the center oval. Have students write one addition strategy in each of the surrounding ovals.

2-1 Skills Practice
Addition Properties

Name _____

Find each sum.

1.	2.	3.
$3 + 2 = 5$	$5 + 7 = 12$	$2 + 0 = 2$
$2 + 3 = 5$	$7 + 5 = 12$	$0 + 2 = 2$

4.	5.	6.
$4 + 5 = 9$	$7 + 0 = 7$	$4 + 2 = 6$
$5 + 4 = 9$	$0 + 7 = 7$	$2 + 4 = 6$

7.	8.	9.
$5 + 6 = 11$	$3 + 4 = 7$	$7 + 4 = 11$
$6 + 5 = 11$	$4 + 3 = 7$	$4 + 7 = 11$

10.	11.	12.
$7 + 2 = 9$	$0 + 3 = 3$	$4 + 6 = 10$
$2 + 7 = 9$	$3 + 0 = 3$	$6 + 4 = 10$

13. $8 + 3 = 11$ 14. $6 + 4 = 10$ 15. $3 + 9 = 12$

$3 + 8 = 11$ $4 + 6 = 10$ $9 + 3 = 12$

Solve.

16. There are 2 brown frogs. There are 8 green frogs. How many frogs are there? __10__ frogs

17. There are 8 spotted turtles. There are 2 striped turtles. How many turtles are there? __10__ turtles

2-1 Reteach
Addition Properties

Name _____

$2 + 3 = 5$
$3 + 2 = 5$

The order of the addends is changed. The sum is the same.

$4 + 0 = 4$
$0 + 4 = 4$

Add 0 to a number. The sum is the same as the other addend.

Find each sum.

1. $8 + 4 = 12$
   $4 + 8 = 12$

2. $5 + 0 = 5$
   $0 + 5 = 5$

3. $3 + 4 = 7$
   $4 + 3 = 7$

4. $1 + 8 = 9$
   $8 + 1 = 9$

5. $5 + 3 = 8$
   $3 + 5 = 8$

6. $6 + 5 = 11$
   $5 + 6 = 11$

Name _____

2-1 Problem-Solving Practice

Addition Properties

Use what you know about addition properties to solve.

1. What two addition facts can April use to find the total number of dots on this domino?

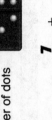

$3 + 7 = 10$

$7 + 3 = 10$

2. What two addition facts can Ken write to match these base-ten blocks?

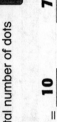

$6 + 5 = 11$

$5 + 6 = 11$

3. Manuel's team scores 8 runs in the first game. They score |||| runs in the second game. Show two ways you can find the total number of runs.

$8 + 4 = 12$

$4 + 8 = 12$

4. Cassie knows that $7 + 0 = 7$. How can she use the same addends to write the fact another way?

$0 + 7 = 7$

5. Emma knows that $4 + 5 = 9$. How can Emma use the same addends to write the fact another way?

$5 + 4 = 9$

Grade 2   9   Chapter 2

Name _____

2-1 Homework Practice

Addition Properties

Find each sum.

1. $\begin{array}{r} 7 \\ +2 \\ \hline 9 \end{array}$ $\begin{array}{r} 2 \\ +7 \\ \hline 9 \end{array}$

2. $\begin{array}{r} 3 \\ +9 \\ \hline 12 \end{array}$ $\begin{array}{r} 9 \\ +3 \\ \hline 12 \end{array}$

3. $\begin{array}{r} 4 \\ +9 \\ \hline 13 \end{array}$ $\begin{array}{r} 9 \\ +4 \\ \hline 13 \end{array}$

4. $\begin{array}{r} 7 \\ +1 \\ \hline 8 \end{array}$ $\begin{array}{r} 1 \\ +7 \\ \hline 8 \end{array}$

5. $7 + 5 = 12$
   $5 + 7 = 12$

6. $6 + 2 = 8$
   $2 + 6 = 8$

7. $1 + 7 = 8$
   $7 + 1 = 8$

8. $5 + 4 = 9$
   $4 + 5 = 9$

Solve.

9. The zoo has 4 striped snakes. It has 2 yellow snakes, too. How many total snakes?

   __6__ snakes

10. There are 2 brown bears. There are 4 black bears. How many bears are there?

    __6__ bears

11. There are 7 blue birds. There are 3 red birds. How many birds are there in all?

    __10__ birds

Grade 2   8   Chapter 2

Grade 2   A3   Chapter 2

Answers (Lessons 2-1 and 2-2)

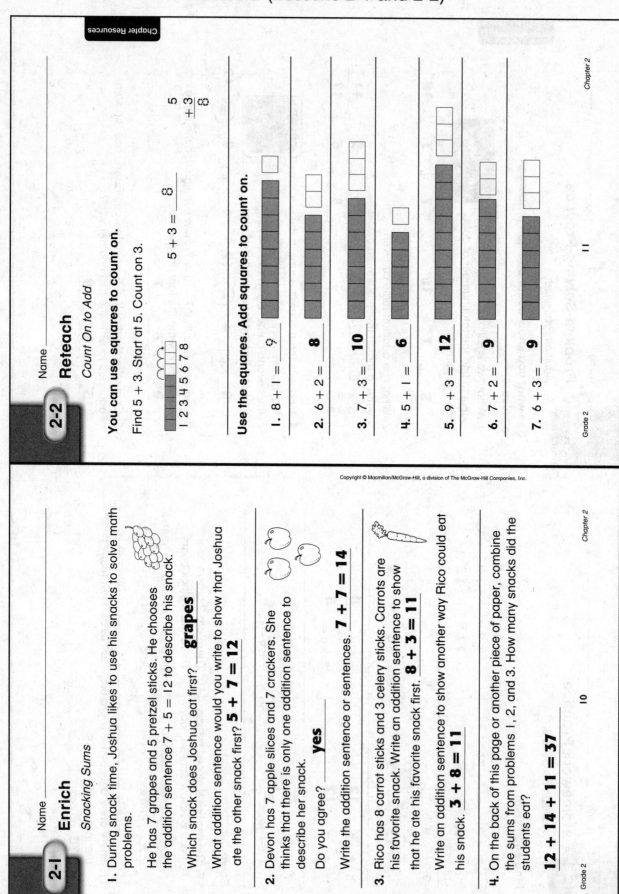

2-2 Reteach
Count On to Add

You can use squares to count on.

Find 5 + 3. Start at 5. Count on 3.

1 2 3 4 5 6 7 8

$$5 + 3 = 8$$

$$\begin{array}{r} 5 \\ +3 \\ \hline 8 \end{array}$$

Use the squares. Add squares to count on.

1. 8 + 1 = 9

2. 6 + 2 = **8**

3. 7 + 3 = **10**

4. 5 + 1 = **6**

5. 9 + 3 = **12**

6. 7 + 2 = **9**

7. 6 + 3 = **9**

Grade 2
Chapter 2
11

2-1 Enrich
Snacking Sums

1. During snack time, Joshua likes to use his snacks to solve math problems.

   He has 7 grapes and 5 pretzel sticks. He chooses the addition sentence 7 + 5 = 12 to describe his snack.

   Which snack does Joshua eat first? **grapes**

   What addition sentence would you write to show that Joshua ate the other snack first? **5 + 7 = 12**

2. Devon has 7 apple slices and 7 crackers. She thinks that there is only one addition sentence to describe her snack.

   Do you agree? **yes**

   Write the addition sentence or sentences. **7 + 7 = 14**

3. Rico has 8 carrot sticks and 3 celery sticks. Carrots are his favorite snack. Write an addition sentence to show that he ate his favorite snack first. **8 + 3 = 11**

   Write an addition sentence to show another way Rico could eat his snack. **3 + 8 = 11**

4. On the back of this page or another piece of paper, combine the sums from problems 1, 2, and 3. How many snacks did the students eat?

   12 + 14 + 11 = 37

Grade 2
Chapter 2
10

2-2 Homework Practice
Count On to Add

1	2	3	4	5
6	7	8	9	10
11	12	13	14	15
16	17	18	19	20
21	22	23	24	25

Use the numbers square. Count on to add.

$$4+1=5 \qquad 2+6=8 \qquad 1+8=9$$

1. $2+4=6 \qquad 2+8=10 \qquad 3+9=12$
2. $1+4=5 \qquad 3+1=4 \qquad 4+6=10$
3. $3+3=6 \qquad 1+6=7 \qquad 4+2=6$

4. $8+3=11 \qquad 9+3=12$
5. $5+2=7 \qquad 6+2=8$
   $7+1=8$
   $2+5=7$

Count on to solve.

6. Ken had 4 fish. Now Ken has 7 fish. How many fish did he buy?
   3 fish

7. Cherie has some trading cards. She gets 3 more cards. Now she has 9. How many cards did she have at the start?
   6 cards

2-2 Skills Practice
Count On to Add

You can use a number line to add.

`0 1 2 3 4 5 6 7 8 9 10 11 12`

1. $6+1=7 \qquad 2+3=5 \qquad 4+3=7$
2. $1+7=8 \qquad 5+2=7 \qquad 6+3=9$

Use the number line. Count on to add.

3. $3+9=12 \qquad 4+3=7 \qquad 7+2=9 \qquad 2+2=4$
4. $8+3=11 \qquad 2+6=8 \qquad 5+1=6 \qquad 5+0=5$
5. $7+3=10 \qquad 1+9=10 \qquad 8+0=8 \qquad 6+3=9$

$4+2=6 \qquad 0+4=4 \qquad 9+2=11 \qquad 3+7=10$

Solve.

6. A frog jumps over 6 rocks. Then he jumps over 2 more. How many rocks does he jump over?
   8 rocks

7. A turtle lays 4 eggs. Then she lays 3 more. How many eggs does she lay in all?
   7 eggs

Answers (Lesson 2-2)

2-2

Name _____

Enrich
Counting Critters

This is an addition square. The sum of the numbers is the same for each row, column, and diagonal. They all equal 15.

First, find the sum of the two numbers in each row. Then use the **count on** strategy to determine the number hidden behind the critter. Write the number in the box at the end of the row.

🐿️	3	8	**4**
🐿️	5	1	**9**
2	🐿️	6	**7**
15	**15**	**15**	**15**

Use the number line to count on.

1 2 3 4 5 6 7 8 9 10 11 12 13 14 15

On the back of this page or on another piece of paper, make your own addition square. The sum of each row, column, and diagonal should be 12. **Answers will vary.**

2-2

Name _____

Problem-Solving Practice
Count On to Add

← 0 1 2 3 4 5 6 7 8 9 10 11 12 →

Count on to add.

1. Linda and Nell put their eggs in a basket. There are 6 eggs in all. Nell put in 4 eggs. How many eggs did Linda put in?

   2 eggs

2. The Brown farm has 2 pigs. There are 5 pigs at the Green farm. How many more pigs do the Greens have?

   3 pigs

3. Sal's cow gives 3 pails of milk in the morning. She gives 5 pails in the afternoon. How much milk does Sal's cow give in one day?

   8 pails

4. A farm grows 4 kinds of green cabbage, 3 kinds of tomatoes, and 2 kinds of red cabbage. How many kinds of cabbage do they grow?

   6 kinds of cabbage

5. Quackers Farm keeps 5 ducks in the front pond. They keep 2 ducks in the back pond. How many ducks are at the farm?

   7 ducks

6. Peter grows 7 kinds of red peppers. His brother grows 2 kinds of green peppers. How many kinds of peppers do they grow in all?

   9 kinds of peppers

7. Mr. Rey's fish farm has 5 tanks. He has 4 tanks of baby fish. He also has adult fish. How many tanks of adult fish does he have?

   1 tanks of adult fish

8. Gus sells 6 bunches of corn. His sister sells 2 bunches of corn. How many bunches of corn did they sell altogether?

   8 bunches

Answers (Lesson 2-3)

Name _____

2-3 Reteach (2)

Problem-Solving Strategy: Act It Out

Solve. Use counters to act it out.

1. Mary sees 1 dog, 4 bees, and 2 swans at the park.
   How many swans does she see?

   ○ ○ ○ ○ ● ● **2** ____ swans

2. 7 cars are in the parking lot. 4 cars leave. 2 more come back.
   How many cars are there now?

   ● ● ● ○ ○ ○ ○ **5** ____ cars

3. Mia saw 4 bears at the zoo. She saw 9 bears on T.V.
   How many bears did she see in all?

   ● ● ● ● ○ ○ ○ ○ ○ ○ ○ ○ ○ **13** ____ bears

4. Kat has 15 balloons. 10 are red. The rest are blue.
   How many blue balloons are there?

   ● ● ● ● ● ● ● ● ● ● ○ ○ ○ ○ ○ **5** ____ blue balloons

5. There are 4 markers in the bin. Rick puts 5 more in the bin.
   How many markers are there altogether?

   9 ____ markers

Name _____

2-3 Reteach (1)

Problem-Solving Strategy: Act It Out

Jeff likes to watch birds on the way to school. Today, he saw 5 crows and 12 robins. How many birds did Jeff see?

Step 1 Understand

What do I know?
Jeff saw 5 crows.
Jeff saw 12 robins.

What do I need to find out?
How many birds did Jeff see?

Step 2 Plan

How will I find how many birds he saw?
I can act it out using **counters** .

Step 3 Solve

Act it out
I can use red counters to stand for robins.
I can use white counters for crows.

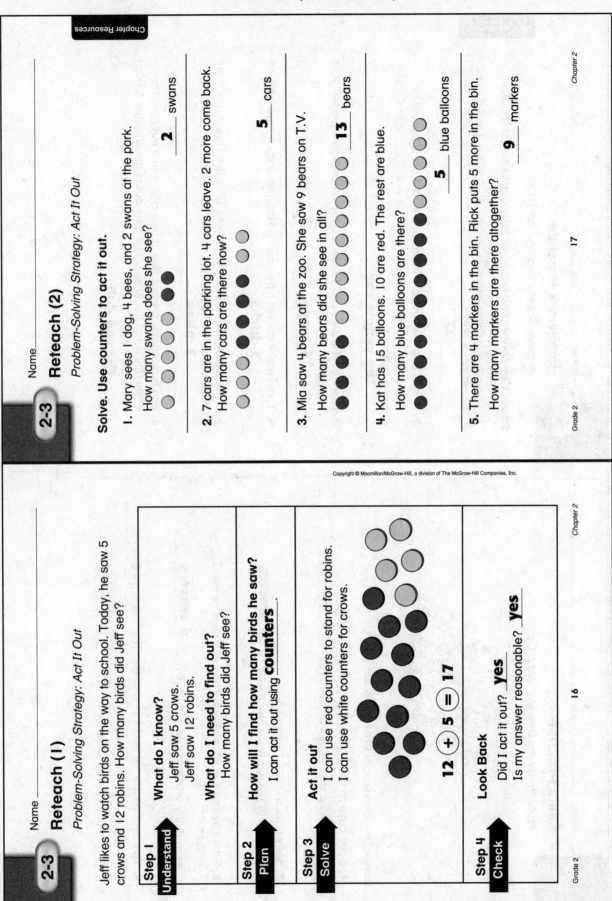

12 + 5 = 17

Step 4 Check

Look Back
Did I act it out? **yes**
Is my answer reasonable? **yes**

Answers (Lesson 2-3)

Name _____

2-3

Homework Practice

Problem-Solving Strategy: Act It Out

Solve. Use connecting cubes or tally marks to act it out.

1. There is a number between 26 and 29. It has a 7 in the ones place. What is it?

    27

2. Randy puts his toy cars in a row. The red car is behind the black car. The black car is behind the yellow car. Which color car is in front?

    the yellow car

3. May has 4 apples and 19 grapes. How many more grapes does she have?

    15 grapes

4. Tom sees 4 ducks. 1 flies away. How many ducks are left?

    3 ducks

5. Betty walked 15 miles. Josh walked 12 miles. How many more miles did Betty walk than Josh?

    3 miles

6. Ella has 3 dolls: a white doll, a blue doll, and a red doll. The white doll is not the tallest. The blue doll is the shortest. Which doll is the tallest?

    the red doll

Chapter 2

19

Grade 2

Name _____

2-3

Skills Practice

Problem-Solving Strategy: Act It Out

Solve. Use classroom erasers to act it out.

1. Scott buys all the 🐘 and 🐻 erasers. How many erasers does he buy in all?   **6 erasers**

2. Kelly buys all the 🐕 erasers. How many erasers does she have?   **7 erasers**

3. Sara buys all the 🐻 erasers. Then she buys all the 🦭 erasers. How many erasers does she have?   **6 erasers**

4. Ted buys all the 🦓 and 🐷 erasers. Then he buys 8 more erasers. How many erasers does he have?   **11 erasers**

Chapter 2

18

Grade 2

2-4

Name

Reteach

Doubles

Addends that are the same are called doubles.

$$3 + 3 = 6$$
addend addend

Add. Use doubles.

1. $4 + 4 = 8$

2. $6 + 6 = 12$

3. $2 + 2 = 4$

4. $5 + 5 = 10$

5. $7 + 7 = 14$

6. $9 + 9 = 18$

2-3

Name

Enrich

Missing Information

Ginny's Gems

Ginny collects shiny beads. She keeps them in round boxes and square boxes. All the round boxes have the same number of beads in them. All the square boxes have the same number of beads in them. Look at the clues to find out how many beads are in each box.

+ = 14 beads

+ = 12 beads

+ + = 22 beads

How many beads are in each round box? __6__

How many beads are in each square box? __8__

Look at these boxes. Which set has more beads? How do you know?

Set A   Set B

Set A has more beads.

$6 + 6 + 6 = 18, 8 + 8 = 16. 18$ is greater than 16.

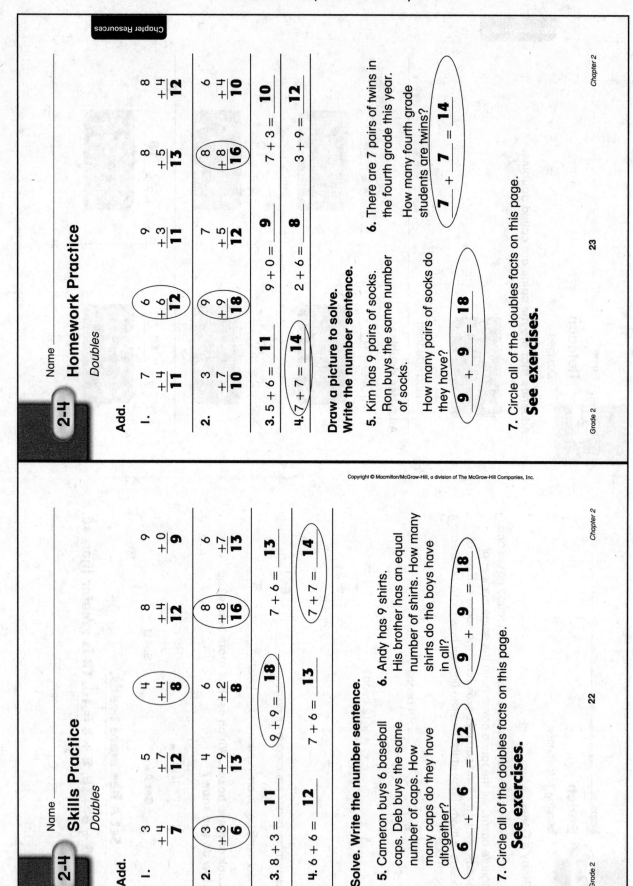

Homework Practice

Name _____

2-4

Homework Practice

Doubles

Add.

1. $7+4=11$ $6+6=12$ (circled) $9+3=11$ $8+5=13$ $8+4=12$

2. $3+7=10$ $9+9=18$ (circled) $7+5=12$ $8+8=16$ (circled) $6+4=10$

3. $5+6=11$ $9+0=9$ $7+3=10$

4. $7+7=14$ (circled) $2+6=8$ $3+9=12$

Draw a picture to solve. Write the number sentence.

5. Kim has 9 pairs of socks. Ron buys the same number of socks. How many pairs of socks do they have? $9+9=18$ (circled)

6. There are 7 pairs of twins in the fourth grade this year. How many fourth grade students are twins? $7+7=14$ (circled)

7. Circle all of the doubles facts on this page. **See exercises.**

Grade 2   23   *Chapter 2*

Skills Practice

Name _____

2-4

Skills Practice

Doubles

Add.

1. $3+4=7$ $3+3=6$ (circled) $5+7=12$ $4+4=8$ (circled) $9+0=9$

2. ... $4+9=13$ $6+2=8$ $8+8=16$ (circled) $6+7=13$

3. $8+3=11$ $9+9=18$ (circled) $7+6=13$

4. $6+6=12$ $7+6=13$ $7+7=14$ (circled)

Solve. Write the number sentence.

5. Cameron buys 6 baseball caps. Deb buys the same number of caps. How many caps do they have altogether? $6+6=12$ (circled)

6. Andy has 9 shirts. His brother has an equal number of shirts. How many shirts do the boys have in all? $9+9=18$ (circled)

7. Circle all of the doubles facts on this page. **See exercises.**

Grade 2   22   *Chapter 2*

Name _____

2-4

Enrich
Dinosaur Doubles

Do all numbers have doubles in their fact families?

Color the dinosaurs blue that have doubles in their fact family.
Color the dinosaurs green that do not have doubles in their fact family.

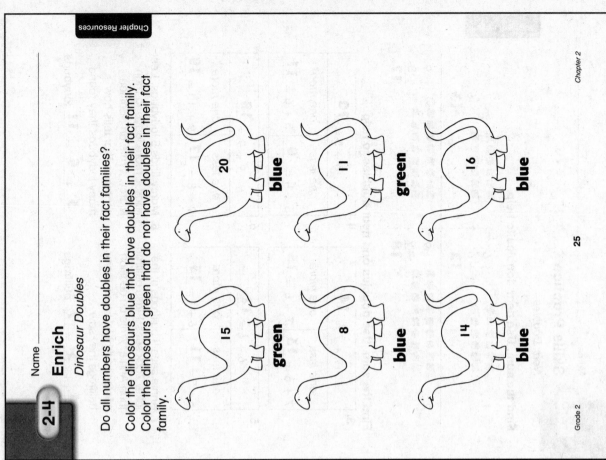

15 — green
8 — blue
14 — blue

20 — blue
11 — green
16 — blue

Name _____

2-4

Problem-Solving Practice
Doubles

Write the number sentence. Use doubles to solve.

1. Terry cut 8 snowflakes from white paper. Derek cut 8 snowflakes from blue paper. How many paper snowflakes did they make?

   $8 + 8 = 16$

2. Mr. Bean sells 5 melons to Ed. He sells the same number of melons to Jose. How many melons did Mr. Bean sell in all?

   $5 + 5 = 10$

3. Carmen has 6 new trading cards. Miguel has an equal number of cards. What is the total number of cards they have?

   $6 + 6 = 12$

4. Lisa finds 9 markers in her room. She finds an equal number in the kitchen. What is the sum of all the markers Lisa found?

   $9 + 9 = 18$

5. Mel works at a shoe store. Monday he sold 10 pairs of shoes. 1 pair equals 2 shoes. How many shoes did Mel sell?

   $10 + 10 = 20$

6. Paula rides the bus to school for 7 blocks. She also rides the bus home. How many blocks does she ride in 1 day?

   $7 + 7 = 14$

7. Claudia is making a rug. It can hold 4 pairs of boots. How many boots will fit on the rug?

   $4 + 4 = 8$

8. Dan used 3 stamps. His mom used 3 more. How many stamps did they use in all?

   $3 + 3 = 6$

Answers

Skills Practice — 2-5

Near Doubles

Find the sum. Use near doubles to help.

1. $6 + 6 = 12$; $7 + 6 = 13$
2. $9 + 9 = 18$; $9 + 8 = 17$

Find the sum. Use doubles and near doubles to help.

3. $7 + 7 = 14$
one more	one less
$7 + 8 = 15$	$7 + 6 = 13$

4. $5 + 5 = 10$
one more	one less
$5 + 6 = 11$	$5 + 4 = 9$

5. $6 + 6 = 12$
one more	one less
$6 + 7 = 13$	$6 + 5 = 11$

6. $9 + 9 = 18$
one more	one less
$9 + 10 = 19$	$9 + 8 = 17$

7. Annie sees 4 bullfrogs at the lake. Zack sees 1 less bullfrog than Annie. Write an addition sentence that tells how many bullfrogs they saw.

   $4 + 3 = 7$ bullfrogs

8. Marcy finds 5 ladybugs. Lee finds 1 more ladybug than Marcy. Write an addition sentence that tells how many ladybugs they found.

   $5 + 6 = 11$ ladybugs

Reteach — 2-5

Near Doubles

Knowing doubles can help you learn other facts.

Think: I know $4 + 4 = 8$

$4 + 4 = 8$

Think: I know $4 + 5$ is one more than $4 + 4$. $4 + 4 = 8$ so $4 + 5 = 9$.

$4 + 5 = 9$

Find the sum. Use doubles to help.

1. $4 + 4 = 8$; $4 + 5 = 9$
2. $6 + 6 = 12$; $6 + 5 = 11$

3. $5 + 5 = 10$; $5 + 6 = 11$
4. $8 + 8 = 16$; $8 + 9 = 17$
5. $6 + 6 = 12$; $6 + 7 = 13$
6. $8 + 8 = 16$; $8 + 7 = 15$
7. $10 + 10 = 20$; $10 + 9 = 19$
8. $7 + 7 = 14$; $7 + 8 = 15$

Chapter Resources

Answers (Lesson 2-5)

Name _____

2-5 Homework Practice

Near Doubles

Find the sum.

1.
```
  [7]
+ [6]
  13
```

```
  [8]
+ [9]
  17
```

2.
```
  7
+ 7
 (14)
```

```
  6
+ 6
 (12)
```

```
  [5]
+ [4]
   9
```

```
  [7]
+ [8]
  15
```

```
  [9]
+ [8]
  17
```

3. 5 + 7 = **12**   9 + 6 = **15**

4. 9 + 9 = **(18)**   [5] + [6] = **11**   [4] + [3] = **7**   8 + 10 = **18**

Use what you know about near doubles to solve.

5. Look at all the sums above. Circle the **sums of doubles**. **See exercises.**

6. Look at the addends above. Draw a box around the addends that are near doubles. **See exercises.**

7. Vik gets 8 dollars for pulling weeds. Anya mows the grass and gets a dollar more than Vik. Write an addition sentence that tells how many dollars Vik and Anya get in an hour.

8 + **9** = **17** dollars

8. Marlene washes 7 pairs of jeans on Tuesday. She washes 1 less pair on Thursday. Write a near double addition sentence to tell the total number of jeans Marlene washes.

7 + **6** = **13** jeans

Grade 2   28   Chapter 2

Name _____

2-5 Problem-Solving Practice

Near Doubles

Use what you know about near doubles to solve.

1. Paula knows she can use two different doubles facts to find the sum of 8 + 9. What are they?

8 + **8** = **16**

9 + **9** = **18**

2. Scotty is looking for two different doubles facts that he can use to find the sum of 7 + 6. What are they?

6 + **6** = **12**

7 + **7** = **14**

3. Chris buys 9 boxes of juice for the baseball team. Allen buys 1 less box than Chris. Write an addition fact to find the total number of boxes Chris and Allen buy.

9 + **8** = **17**

4. One store gives 6 baseball mitts to the team. Another store gives 1 more mitt than the first. Write an addition fact that tells the total number of mitts.

6 + **7** = **13**

5. Mr. Gomez buys 4 new bats for the team. Mr. Moore buys 1 more bat than Mr. Gomez. What is the total number of bats they give?

4 + **5** = **9**

6. On Wednesday, the Reed family buys 7 tickets to the game. On Thursday, they buy 1 more ticket than they did on Wednesday. How many tickets does the Reed family have?

7 + **8** = **15**

7. This year the Tigers made 1 more goal than they made last year. Last year they made 8 goals. How many goals did they make in both years?

9 + **8** = **17**

Grade 2   29   Chapter 2

Answers

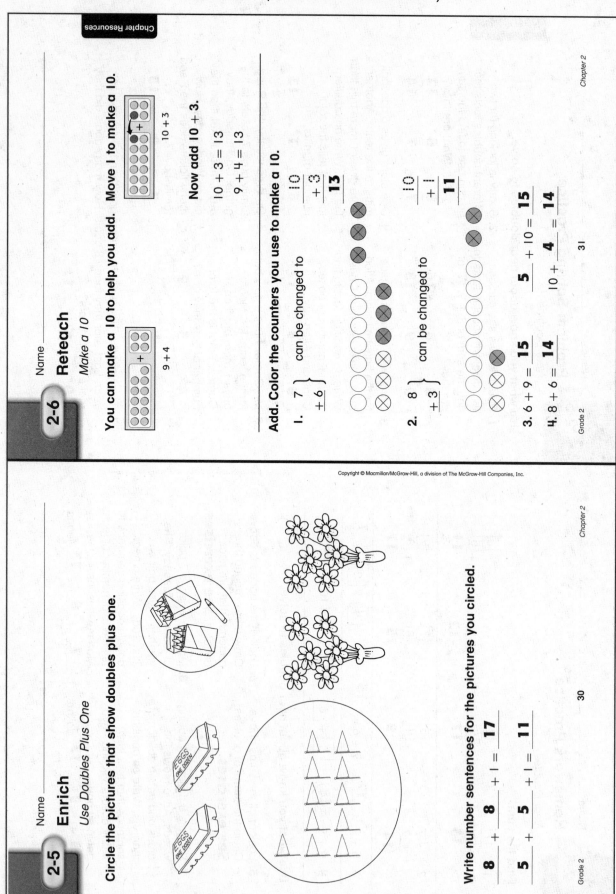

2-6

Name

Reteach
Make a 10

You can make a 10 to help you add.   **Move 1 to make a 10.**

9 + 4   10 + 3

Now add 10 + 3.

10 + 3 = 13
9 + 4 = 13

Add. Color the counters you use to make a 10.

1. $\begin{array}{r} 7 \\ +6 \\ \hline 13 \end{array}$ can be changed to $\begin{array}{r} 10 \\ +3 \\ \hline 13 \end{array}$

2. $\begin{array}{r} 8 \\ +3 \\ \hline 11 \end{array}$ can be changed to $\begin{array}{r} 11 \\ +\underline{\ \ } \\ \hline 11 \end{array}$

3. 6 + 9 = **15**   5 + 10 = **15**

4. 8 + 6 = **14**   10 + 4 = **14**

Grade 2   31   Chapter 2

2-5

Name

Enrich
Use Doubles Plus One

Circle the pictures that show doubles plus one.

Write number sentences for the pictures you circled.

8 + **8** + 1 = **17**

5 + **5** + 1 = **11**

Grade 2   30   Chapter 2

Answers (Lesson 2-6)

Skills Practice

Make a 10

2-6

Name _____

Add. Use connecting cubes to help.

1.

$$\begin{array}{r} 8 \\ + 6 \\ \hline 14 \end{array}$$

can be changed to

$$\begin{array}{r} 10 \\ + 4 \\ \hline 14 \end{array}$$

2.
$$\begin{array}{r} 7 \\ + 7 \\ \hline 14 \end{array} \qquad \begin{array}{r} 8 \\ + 6 \\ \hline 14 \end{array} \qquad \begin{array}{r} 9 \\ + 5 \\ \hline 14 \end{array} \qquad \begin{array}{r} 9 \\ + 4 \\ \hline 13 \end{array} \qquad \begin{array}{r} 8 \\ + 4 \\ \hline 12 \end{array}$$

3. $7 + 4 = \underline{11}$ $\qquad 8 + 8 = \underline{16}$ $\qquad 7 + 8 = \underline{15}$

4. $9 + 7 = \underline{16}$ $\qquad 6 + 7 = \underline{13}$ $\qquad 8 + 9 = \underline{17}$

Solve.

5. Ali built 8 model airplanes in October. In November she built 6 model airplanes. How many airplanes has she built in all?

$\underline{8} + \underline{6} = \underline{14}$.

6. Marty learned to play 7 new songs in January. In February, he learned 5 new songs.

How many songs has he learned in the two months?

$\underline{7} + \underline{5} = \underline{12}$

Grade 2 · Chapter 2 · 32

Homework Practice

Make a 10

2-6

Name _____

Add. Remember to make a 10 first.

1.
$$\begin{array}{r} 7 \\ + 4 \\ \hline 11 \end{array} \qquad \begin{array}{r} 4 \\ + 8 \\ \hline 12 \end{array} \qquad \begin{array}{r} 9 \\ + 7 \\ \hline 16 \end{array} \qquad \begin{array}{r} \boxed{7} \\ + 6 \\ \hline 13 \end{array} \qquad \begin{array}{r} 2 \\ + 9 \\ \hline 11 \end{array}$$

2.
$$\begin{array}{r} 3 \\ + 9 \\ \hline 12 \end{array} \qquad \begin{array}{r} 7 \\ + 5 \\ \hline 12 \end{array} \qquad \begin{array}{r} 8 \\ + 8 \\ \hline 16 \end{array} \qquad \begin{array}{r} 9 \\ + 4 \\ \hline 13 \end{array} \qquad \begin{array}{r} \boxed{8} \\ + 7 \\ \hline 15 \end{array}$$

3. $7 + 7 = \underline{14}$ $\qquad 4 + 8 = \underline{12}$ $\qquad 9 + 5 = \underline{14}$

4. $\boxed{8} + \boxed{9} = \underline{17}$ $\qquad 9 + 7 = \underline{16}$ $\qquad 6 + 9 = \underline{15}$

5. Look at the addends in the questions above. Circle any addends that you can add using near doubles. **See exercises**

Solve. Remember to first make a 10.

6. Raul wins 8 chess matches on Saturday. He wins 5 matches on Sunday. Complete the two addition sentences to show how many games he won all weekend.

$8 + \underline{5} = \underline{13}$

$\underline{10} + \underline{3} = \underline{13}$

7. Carla's team won 6 games last year. This year, her team has won 9 games. Complete the two addition sentences to show how many games her team won both years.

$6 + \underline{9} = \underline{15}$

$\underline{5} + \underline{10} = \underline{15}$

8. Show how you would explain "Make a 10" to someone who had never heard of it. **Accept any reasonable explanation.**

Grade 2 · Chapter 2 · 33

Chapter Resources

Answers

Copyright © Macmillan/McGraw-Hill, a division of The McGraw-Hill Companies, Inc.

Grade 2 · A15

2-6

Name

Problem-Solving Practice

Make a 10

Solve.

1. Mel bakes 6 loaves of bread for the bake sale. His sister bakes 8 loaves.

   How many loaves of bread will they bring to the bake sale?

   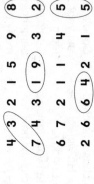

   $8 + \underline{6} = \underline{14}$

2. Pauline's mom makes 7 pies for the bake sale. Ann's mom makes 9 pies.

   How many pies will they bring to the bake sale?

   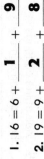

   $7 + \underline{9} = \underline{16}$

3. Ms. Ling uses part of the money from the bake sale to buy art supplies. She buys 5 boxes of red markers and 8 boxes of blue markers.

   How many boxes of markers did she buy in all?

   $\underline{13}$ boxes of markers

4. Mrs. Quinn buys some pencils. Mr. Lopez buys 7 boxes of pencils. Together they bought 15 boxes.

   How many boxes of pencils did Mrs. Quinn buy?

   $\underline{8}$ boxes of pencils

5. David's class sent 9 letters to the president. Ann's class also sent letters. The two classes sent 17 letters in all.

   How many letters did Ann's class send?

   $\underline{8}$ letters

6. Mrs. Han's class has 5 fish in their fish tank. Ms. Johnson's class has 9 fish in their tank.

   How many more fish does Ms. Johnson's class have?

   $\underline{4}$ fish

Grade 2   34   Chapter 2

2-6

Name

Enrich

The Top Ten

Circle 5 combinations of two numbers that equal 10. Then fill in the blanks to solve the problems.

Possible answer:

```
4  3  2  1  5  9  8
7  4  3  1  9  3  2
6  7  2  1  1  4  5
2  6  6  4  2  1  5
```

1. $16 = 6 + \underline{1} + \underline{9}$

2. $19 = 9 + \underline{2} + \underline{8}$

3. $20 = 10 + \underline{3} + \underline{7}$

4. $14 = 4 + \underline{4} + \underline{6}$

5. $18 = 8 + \underline{5} + \underline{5}$

Now find combinations of three numbers to solve these problems.

Answers will vary.

6. $\underline{} + \underline{} + \underline{} = 17$

7. $\underline{} + \underline{} + \underline{} = 19$

8. $\underline{} + \underline{} + \underline{} = 12$

Grade 2   35   Chapter 2

Name

2-7 Skills Practice
Add Three Numbers

Find each sum.

1.
$$\begin{array}{r}3\\2\\+3\\\hline 8\end{array}\quad\begin{array}{r}4\\5\\+4\\\hline 13\end{array}\quad\begin{array}{r}8\\0\\+2\\\hline 10\end{array}\quad\begin{array}{r}4\\3\\+4\\\hline 11\end{array}\quad\begin{array}{r}5\\4\\+6\\\hline 15\end{array}\quad\begin{array}{r}9\\1\\+5\\\hline 15\end{array}$$

2.
$$\begin{array}{r}4\\8\\+2\\\hline 14\end{array}\quad\begin{array}{r}7\\6\\+6\\\hline 19\end{array}\quad\begin{array}{r}9\\1\\+4\\\hline 14\end{array}\quad\begin{array}{r}8\\3\\+8\\\hline 19\end{array}\quad\begin{array}{r}7\\3\\+6\\\hline 16\end{array}\quad\begin{array}{r}5\\5\\+5\\\hline 15\end{array}$$

3.
$$\begin{array}{r}4\\6\\+8\\\hline 18\end{array}\quad\begin{array}{r}3\\5\\+3\\\hline 11\end{array}\quad\begin{array}{r}0\\7\\+7\\\hline 14\end{array}\quad\begin{array}{r}2\\4\\+8\\\hline 14\end{array}\quad\begin{array}{r}8\\2\\+3\\\hline 13\end{array}\quad\begin{array}{r}3\\6\\+7\\\hline 16\end{array}$$

4.
$$\begin{array}{r}6\\5\\+6\\\hline 17\end{array}\quad\begin{array}{r}4\\4\\+7\\\hline 15\end{array}\quad\begin{array}{r}8\\2\\+4\\\hline 14\end{array}\quad\begin{array}{r}5\\3\\+5\\\hline 13\end{array}\quad\begin{array}{r}1\\9\\+6\\\hline 16\end{array}\quad\begin{array}{r}3\\8\\+2\\\hline 13\end{array}$$

Solve.

5. Jan has 4 stamps. Tim has 9 stamps. Ben has 4 stamps. How many total stamps do they have? __17__ stamps

6. There are 4 bear stickers, 6 wolf stickers, and 8 fox stickers. How many stickers are there in all? __18__ stickers

Name

2-7 Reteach
Add Three Numbers

You can group addends.
You can use doubles or make a 10.

Find a double.
$$\begin{array}{r}4\\3\\+4\end{array}\;\begin{array}{r}3\\8\\+3\end{array}$$

Make a 10.
$$\begin{array}{r}6\\5\\+4\end{array}\;\begin{array}{r}5\\10\\+5\\\hline 15\end{array}$$

Find a double. Circle addends that make doubles. Add.

1. (3)(3) +7 → 6 +7 = 13
(4)4 5 +4 → 8
(2)4 (2) + = 8
3(5) 7 (3)+6 = 13 ... 7 +8 = 13

Make a 10. Circle addends that make a 10. Add.

2. (8)(2) +4 → 10 +4 = 14
(4)3 (6) + = 13... 3(10)+4 = 13
8(8) (7)10 (3)+ = 18... 8(10)+6 = 16
(1)(9)4 + = 14

Find the sum.

3. 8 3 +8 = 19
9 9 +1 = 18
9 9 +2 = 20
8 7 +2 = 17
7 0 +8 = 16

Answers (Lesson 2-7)

2-7

Name _____

Problem-Solving Practice

Add Three Numbers

Complete the number sentence. Find each sum.

1. The zoo has 5 black bears, 5 brown bears, and 2 polar bears. How many bears are at the zoo?

   $5 + 5 + 2 = 12$ bears

2. In the baby zoo, 2 cubs are playing, 3 cubs are sleeping, and 3 cubs are eating. How many cubs are at the baby zoo?

   $2 + 3 + 3 = 8$ cubs

3. Ellie feeds 3 lambs and 4 goats. Tom feeds 7 ducks. How many animals did they feed in all.

   $3 + 4 + 7 = 14$ animals

4. 6 seals are on the high rocks. 4 seals and 3 seagulls are on the low rocks. 5 seals are in the water. How many seals are there in all?

   $6 + 4 + 5 = 15$ seals

5. Eric draws 1 lion, 6 birds, 1 tree, 2 houses, and 6 deer. How many animals does he draw altogether?

   $1 + 6 + 6 = 13$ animals

6. There are 9 boys, 3 teachers, 2 dogs, and 7 girls watching the water show. How many people are watching the show in all?

   $9 + 3 + 7 = 19$ people

39

2-7

Name _____

Homework Practice

Add Three Numbers

Find each sum.

1.
$$\begin{array}{r} 6 \\ 5 \\ +4 \\ \hline 15 \end{array} \qquad \begin{array}{r} 6 \\ 2 \\ +8 \\ \hline 16 \end{array} \qquad \begin{array}{r} 3 \\ 3 \\ +9 \\ \hline 15 \end{array} \qquad \begin{array}{r} 7 \\ 4 \\ +3 \\ \hline 14 \end{array} \qquad \begin{array}{r} 6 \\ 4 \\ +5 \\ \hline 15 \end{array}$$

2.
$$\begin{array}{r} 1 \\ 9 \\ +4 \\ \hline 14 \end{array} \qquad \begin{array}{r} 3 \\ 3 \\ +0 \\ \hline 6 \end{array} \qquad \begin{array}{r} 7 \\ 6 \\ +6 \\ \hline 19 \end{array} \qquad \begin{array}{r} 8 \\ 4 \\ +2 \\ \hline 14 \end{array} \qquad \begin{array}{r} 6 \\ 4 \\ +0 \\ \hline 10 \end{array}$$

3.
$$\begin{array}{r} 7 \\ 3 \\ +5 \\ \hline 15 \end{array} \qquad \begin{array}{r} 6 \\ 1 \\ +6 \\ \hline 13 \end{array} \qquad \begin{array}{r} 4 \\ 2 \\ +6 \\ \hline 12 \end{array} \qquad \begin{array}{r} 9 \\ 8 \\ +1 \\ \hline 18 \end{array} \qquad \begin{array}{r} 6 \\ 6 \\ +6 \\ \hline 18 \end{array}$$

4.
$$\begin{array}{r} 7 \\ 3 \\ +3 \\ \hline 13 \end{array} \qquad \begin{array}{r} 6 \\ 1 \\ +6 \\ \hline 13 \end{array} \qquad \begin{array}{r} 8 \\ 4 \\ +2 \\ \hline 14 \end{array} \qquad \begin{array}{r} 7 \\ 8 \\ +2 \\ \hline 17 \end{array} \qquad \begin{array}{r} 7 \\ 6 \\ +3 \\ \hline 16 \end{array}$$

Solve.

5. Benji has 6 fish. TJ has 7 fish and 3 dogs. Max has 4 fish. How many fish are there?

   17 fish

6. The doctor's office has fish tanks. 5 of the fish are guppies. 6 fish are angel fish. 8 fish are mollies. How many fish in all?

   19 fish

38

Name _____

2-8 Reteach (I)

Problem-Solving Investigation: Choose a Strategy

Jen: It takes me 10 minutes to clean my room.
It takes me 2 minutes to brush my teeth.
It takes me 5 minutes to change my clothes.
How long will it take me to get ready for bed?

Choose a strategy to solve.

Step I **Understand**

What do I know?

First step takes **10** minutes.

Next step takes **2** minutes.

Last step takes **5** minutes.

What do I need to find?

How much time in all will it take?

Step 2 **Plan**

How will I find how much time?

I can **draw a picture** .

Step 3 **Solve**

Draw a picture.

Step 1 room ⅢⅢ ⅢⅢ
Step 2 teeth ⅢⅢ
Step 3 change II

It will take me **17** minutes.

Step 4 **Check**

Did I draw a picture showing three
parts? **yes**
Is my answer reasonable? **yes**

Grade 2

41

Chapter 2

Name _____

2-7 Enrich

Finish Line

**How fast can you add numbers
in your head?**

**Write the subtotals in the squares.
See how quickly you can find
the sums.**

1. $2 + 2 + 1 =$ [**5**] $+ 6 =$ **11**

2. $1 + 1 + 7 =$ [**10**] $+ 9 =$ **19**

3. $3 + 3 + 1 =$ [**7**] $+ 8 =$ **15**

4. $4 + 1 + 1 + 1 =$ [**7**] $+ 10 =$ **17**

5. $2 + 8 + 5 =$ [**15**] $+ 5 =$ **20**

6. $6 + 1 + 1 + 1 + 1 =$ [**10**] $+ 4 =$ **14**

7. Which answer is the greatest? **20**

8. Arrange the answers in order from *least to greatest.*

11 , **14** , **15** , **17** , **19** , **20**

Grade 2

40

Chapter 2

Grade 2

A19

Chapter 2

Name _____

2-8

Skills Practice
Problem-Solving Investigation: Choose a Strategy

Problem-Solving Strategies
Draw a picture
Use logical reasoning
Act it out

Choose a strategy and solve.

Show your work here.

Check students' work.

1. Mrs. Adler washes 4 sweaters on Monday. On Tuesday, Mr. Adler washes 1 less sweater. How many sweaters have the Adlers washed in all?

7 sweaters

2. Ken has 2 blue shirts, 3 white shirts, and 7 striped shirts. How many total shirts does he have?

12 shirts

3. Linda is sewing beads onto her favorite hat. She uses 4 silver beads, 4 clear beads, and 6 gold beads. How many beads in all does Linda use?

14 beads

Name _____

2-8

Reteach (2)
Problem-Solving Investigation: Choose a Strategy

Problem-Solving Strategies
Use logical reasoning
Act it out
Draw a picture

Choose a strategy and solve.

Show your work here.

Check students' work.

1. Candy, Dennis, and Serena are trading CDs. Candy gives 6 CDs to Serena and 5 CDs to Dennis. She has 6 CDs left over. How many CDs did she start with?

17 CDs

2. Keith has 4 drums. Shawn has the same number of drums. How many drums do they have in all?

8 drums

3. The band practices 6 hours a week. There was a 3-hour practice on Monday. How many hours are left to practice this week?

3 hours

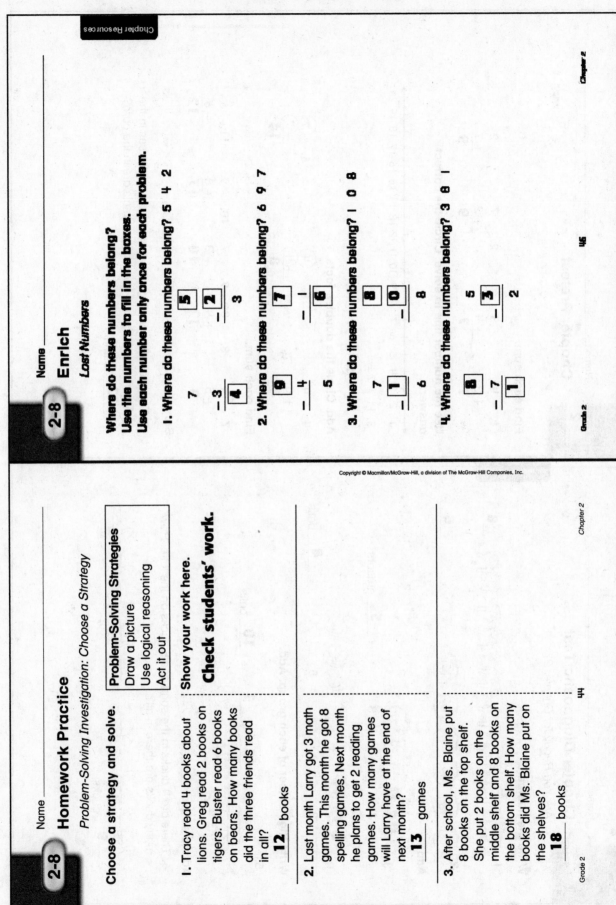

Name _____

2-8

Enrich

Lost Numbers

Where do these numbers belong?
Use the numbers to fill in the boxes.
Use each number only once for each problem.

1. Where do these numbers belong? 5 4 2

$$7 \qquad \boxed{5}$$
$$-3 \qquad -\boxed{2}$$
$$\boxed{4} \qquad 3$$

2. Where do these numbers belong? 6 9 7

$$\boxed{9} \qquad \boxed{7}$$
$$-4 \qquad -\boxed{6}$$
$$5 \qquad 1$$

3. Where do these numbers belong? 1 0 8

$$7 \qquad \boxed{8}$$
$$-\boxed{1} \qquad -\boxed{0}$$
$$6 \qquad 8$$

4. Where do these numbers belong? 3 8 1

$$\boxed{8} \qquad 5$$
$$-7 \qquad -\boxed{3}$$
$$\boxed{1} \qquad 2$$

Grade 2

45

Chapter 2

Name _____

2-8

Homework Practice

Problem-Solving Investigation: Choose a Strategy

Choose a strategy and solve.

Problem-Solving Strategies
Draw a picture
Use logical reasoning
Act it out

Show your work here.
Check students' work.

1. Tracy read 4 books about lions. Greg read 2 books on tigers. Buster read 6 books on bears. How many books did the three friends read in all?

12 books

2. Last month Larry got 3 math games. This month he got 8 spelling games. Next month he plans to get 2 reading games. How many games will Larry have at the end of next month?

13 games

3. After school, Ms. Blaine put 8 books on the top shelf. She put 2 books on the middle shelf and 8 books on the bottom shelf. How many books did Ms. Blaine put on the shelves?

18 books

Grade 2

44

Chapter 2

Grade 2

A21

Chapter 2

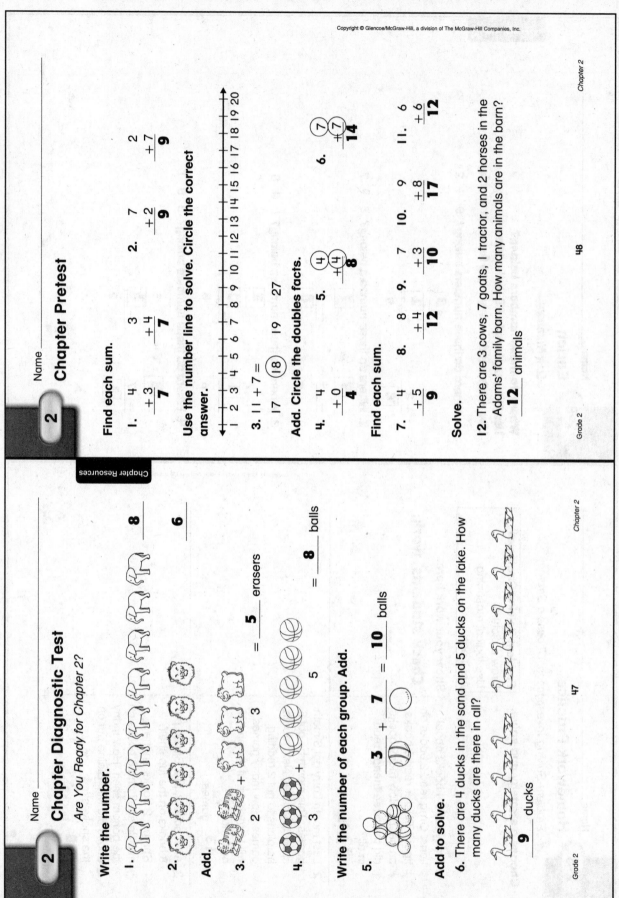

Chapter Pretest

Name

2

Find each sum.

1. $\begin{array}{r} 4 \\ +3 \\ \hline 7 \end{array}$
2. $\begin{array}{r} 3 \\ +4 \\ \hline 7 \end{array}$
   $\begin{array}{r} 7 \\ +2 \\ \hline 9 \end{array}$

Use the number line to solve. Circle the correct answer.

1 2 3 4 5 6 7 8 9 10 11 12 13 14 15 16 17 18 19 20

3. $11 + 7 =$ 17   (18)   19   27

Add. Circle the doubles facts.

4. $\begin{array}{r} 4 \\ +0 \\ \hline 4 \end{array}$
5. $\boxed{\begin{array}{r} 4 \\ +4 \\ \hline 8 \end{array}}$
6. $\boxed{\begin{array}{r} 7 \\ +7 \\ \hline 14 \end{array}}$

Find each sum.

7. $\begin{array}{r} 4 \\ +5 \\ \hline 9 \end{array}$
8. $\begin{array}{r} 8 \\ +4 \\ \hline 12 \end{array}$
9. $\begin{array}{r} 7 \\ +3 \\ \hline 10 \end{array}$
10. $\begin{array}{r} 9 \\ +8 \\ \hline 17 \end{array}$
11. $\begin{array}{r} 6 \\ +6 \\ \hline 12 \end{array}$

Solve.

12. There are 3 cows, 7 goats, 1 tractor, and 2 horses in the Adams' family barn. How many animals are in the barn?

    12 animals

Chapter Diagnostic Test

Name

2

Are You Ready for Chapter 2?

Chapter Resources

Write the number.

1. **8**

2. **6**

Add.

3. $2 + 3 =$ **5** erasers

4. $3 + 5 =$ **8** balls

Write the number of each group. Add.

5. $3 + 7 =$ **10** balls

Add to solve.

6. There are 4 ducks in the sand and 5 ducks on the lake. How many ducks are there in all?

   9 ducks

Answers (Mid-Chapter Test, Vocabulary Test)

Mid-Chapter Test

Name _____

2

Find each sum.

1. $5 + 3 = \mathbf{8}$ 2. $7 + 8 = \mathbf{15}$

$3 + 5 = \mathbf{8}$ $8 + 7 = \mathbf{15}$

Use the number line. Count on to add. Circle the answer.

1 2 3 4 5 6 7 8 9 10 11 12 13 14 15 16 17 18 19 20

3. $12 + 6 =$ 13 (18) 19

4. $11 + 8 =$ 11 18 (19)   18

Add. Circle the doubles facts.

5. $4 + 6 = \mathbf{10}$ 6. $8 + 4 = \mathbf{12}$ 7. $(6) + (6) = \mathbf{12}$ 8. $9 + 0 = \mathbf{9}$

9. $(9) + (9) = \mathbf{18}$ 10. $1 + 6 = \mathbf{7}$ 11. $5 + 4 = \mathbf{9}$ 12. $(7) + (7) = \mathbf{14}$

Solve.

13. Amy buys 7 peaches. Lisa buys 1 more than Amy. How many peaches do they buy in all?

15 peaches

Grade 2   49   Chapter 2

Vocabulary Test

Name _____

2

Use the words in the box.
Write the correct word(s) on the blank.

| doubles |
| addends |
| sum |
| make a 10 |

1. In the number sentence $4 + 5 = 9$, the numbers 4 and 5 are the **addends** .

2. When you add numbers you find the **sum** .

3. Two addends that are the same number are called **doubles** .

4. One strategy for finding a sum is called **make a 10** .

Circle the correct example.

5. doubles plus 1
   $6 + 6$ $5 + 7$ (7 + 8)

6. changing order of addends
   $7 + 0 = 7$ $4 + 4 = 8$
   $8 + 0 = 8$ $6 + 6 = 12$
   $(5 + 9 = 14)$ $(9 + 5 = 14)$

7. counting on

   1 2 3 4 5 6 7 8 9 10 11 12 13 14 15 16 17 18 19 20
   $7 + 5 =$

   1 2 3 4 5 6 7 8 9 10 11 12 13 14 15 16 17 18 19 20
   $(7 + 5 =)$

   1 2 3 4 5 6 7 8 9 10 11 12 13 14 15 16 17 18 19 20
   $7 + 5 =$

Grade 2   50   Chapter 2

Answers

Answers (Oral & Listening Assessment Response Sheets)

Name _____

Listening Assessment Response Sheet

2

Show your model here

$3 + 7 = 10$

$7 + 3 = 10$

$7 + 7 = 14$

$7 + 8 = 15$

Doubles

1. **The order of addends does not change the sum.**

2. _____ doubles _____
   _____ 15 > 14 _____

3. _____ 14, fourteen _____

4. Draw your number line here.

1 2 3 4 5 6 7 8 9 10 11 12 13 14 15 16 17 18 19 20

Name _____

Oral Assessment Response Sheet

2

1. $5 + 5 = 10$ $6 + 4 = 10$ $4 + 6 = 10$ $8 + 2 = 10$

2. $5 + 5 = 10$

3. $4 + 6 = 10$ and $6 + 4 = 10$; The order of addends does not change the sum.

4. $5 + 5 = 10$; Students should indicate understanding of the doubles plus 1 strategy.

5. $8 + 2 = 10$; Students should indicate understanding of the make a 10 strategy.

6. 1 2 3 4 5 6 7 8 9 10 11 12 13 14 15 16 17 18 19 20

7. **13** baskets

Answers

2 Chapter Test, Form I

Name _____

Read each question carefully.
Fill in the circle for the correct answer.

1. 9 + 2 = ☐
- ○ 99 **conceptual error**
- ○ 92 **conceptual error**
- ○ 29 **conceptual error**
- ● 11 **correct**

2. Which is another way to write 6 + 7 = 13?
- ○ 6 + 6 = 12 **conceptual error**
- ● 7 + 6 = 13 **correct**
- ○ 7 + 7 = 14 **conceptual error**
- ○ 10 + 4 = 14 **procedural error**

3. 9 + 0 = ☐
- ○ 0 **conceptual error**
- ● 9 **correct**
- ○ 10 **guess**
- ○ 90 **conceptual error**

4. 6 + 3 =
- ○ 3 **procedural error**
- ○ 6 **procedural error**
- ● 9 **correct**
- ○ 63 **conceptual error**

5. Which addition fact is shown?

7 8 9 10 11 12 13 14

- ○ 7 + 7 = 14 **conceptual error**
- ○ 8 + 1 = 12 **conceptual error**
- ○ 8 + 6 = 14 **guess**
- ● 8 + 4 = 12 **correct**

6. What doubles fact can help you find the sum of 5 + 6?
- ○ 2 + 2 = 4 **guess**
- ● 5 + 5 = 10 **correct**
- ○ 6 + 5 = 11 **conceptual error**
- ○ 7 + 7 = 14 **conceptual error**

GO ON

Chapter Resources

Name _____

2 Chapter Test, Form I (continued)

7. There are 8 cows in the field. There are 2 fewer cows in the barn. Which number sentence tells how many cows there are in all?

- ○ 8 − 2 = 6 **conceptual error**
- ○ 8 + 2 = 10 **procedural error**
- ● 8 + 6 = 14 **correct**
- ○ 8 + 8 = 16 **guess**

8. Which addition fact can help you find the sum 9 + 6?

- ○ 10 + 6 = 16 **procedural error**
- ○ 10 + 9 = 19 **procedural error**
- ● 10 + 5 = 15 **correct**
- ○ 10 + 1 = 11 **conceptual error**

9. Find the sum.

$$\begin{array}{r} 7 \\ 3 \\ +5 \\ \hline \end{array}$$

- ○ 8 **guess**
- ○ 10 **procedural error**
- ● 15 **correct**
- ○ 17 **procedural error**

10. Add. 4 + 9 + 7 = ☐

- ○ 11 **conceptual error**
- ○ 13 **procedural error**
- ○ 16 **procedural error**
- ● 20 **correct**

STOP

Answers (Chapter Test, Form 2A)

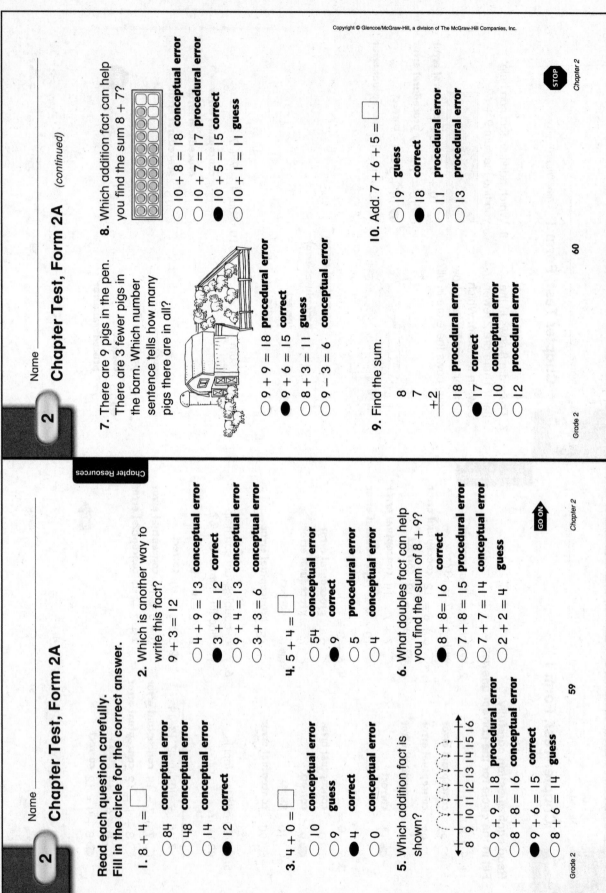

Name _____

2 Chapter Test, Form 2A

Read each question carefully.
Fill in the circle for the correct answer.

1. 8 + 4 = [ ]
○ 84 conceptual error
○ 48 conceptual error
○ 14 conceptual error
● 12 correct

2. Which is another way to write this fact?
9 + 3 = 12
○ 4 + 9 = 13 conceptual error
● 3 + 9 = 12 correct
○ 9 + 4 = 13 conceptual error
○ 3 + 3 = 6 conceptual error

3. 4 + 0 = [ ]
○ 10 conceptual error
○ 9 guess
● 4 correct
○ 0 conceptual error

4. 5 + 4 = [ ]
○ 54 conceptual error
● 9 correct
○ 5 procedural error
○ 4 conceptual error

5. Which addition fact is shown?
8 9 10 11 12 13 14 15 16
○ 9 + 9 = 18 procedural error
● 8 + 8 = 16 conceptual error
○ 9 + 6 = 15 correct
○ 8 + 6 = 14 guess

6. What doubles fact can help you find the sum of 8 + 9?
● 8 + 8 = 16 correct
○ 7 + 8 = 15 procedural error
○ 7 + 7 = 14 conceptual error
○ 2 + 2 = 4 guess

GO ON

Chapter 2

Grade 2

59

Name _____

2 Chapter Test, Form 2A (continued)

7. There are 9 pigs in the pen. There are 3 fewer pigs in the barn. Which number sentence tells how many pigs there are in all?
○ 9 + 9 = 18 procedural error
● 9 + 6 = 15 correct
○ 8 + 3 = 11 guess
○ 9 − 3 = 6 conceptual error

8. Which addition fact can help you find the sum 8 + 7?
○ 10 + 8 = 18 conceptual error
○ 10 + 7 = 17 procedural error
● 10 + 5 = 15 correct
○ 10 + 1 = 11 guess

9. Find the sum.

$$\begin{array}{r} 8 \\ 7 \\ +\,2 \\ \hline \end{array}$$

○ 18 procedural error
● 17 correct
○ 10 conceptual error
○ 12 procedural error

10. Add. 7 + 6 + 5 = [ ]
○ 19 guess
● 18 correct
○ 11 procedural error
○ 13 procedural error

STOP

Chapter 2

Grade 2

60

Chapter Resources

Answers (Chapter Test, Form 2B)

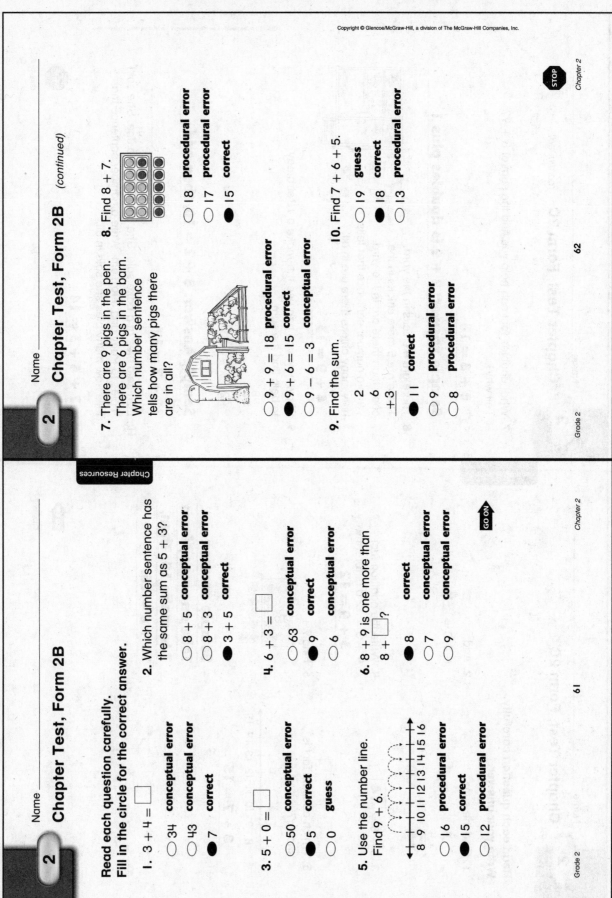

Name _____

2 Chapter Test, Form 2B

Read each question carefully.
Fill in the circle for the correct answer.

1. 3 + 4 = □
○ 34 **conceptual error**
○ 43 **conceptual error**
● 7 **correct**

2. Which number sentence has the same sum as 5 + 3?
○ 8 + 5 **conceptual error**
○ 8 + 3 **conceptual error**
● 3 + 5 **correct**

3. 5 + 0 = □
○ 50 **conceptual error**
● 5 **correct**
○ 0 **guess**

4. 6 + 3 = □
○ 63 **conceptual error**
● 9 **correct**
○ 6 **conceptual error**

5. Use the number line. Find 9 + 6.
(number line: 8 9 10 11 12 13 14 15 16)
○ 16 **procedural error**
● 15 **correct**
○ 12 **procedural error**

6. 8 + 9 is one more than 8 + □?
● 8 **correct**
○ 7 **conceptual error**
○ 9 **conceptual error**

GO ON

Name _____

2 Chapter Test, Form 2B (continued)

7. There are 9 pigs in the pen. There are 6 pigs in the barn. Which number sentence tells how many pigs there are in all?
○ 9 + 9 = 18 **procedural error**
● 9 + 6 = 15 **correct**
○ 9 - 6 = 3 **conceptual error**

8. Find 8 + 7.
○ 18 **procedural error**
○ 17 **procedural error**
● 15 **correct**

9. Find the sum.

$$\begin{array}{r} 2 \\ 6 \\ +3 \\ \hline \end{array}$$

● 11 **correct**
○ 9 **procedural error**
○ 8 **procedural error**

10. Find 7 + 6 + 5.
○ 19 **guess**
● 18 **correct**
○ 13 **procedural error**

STOP

Chapter Resources

Answers

Answers (Chapter Test, Form 2C)

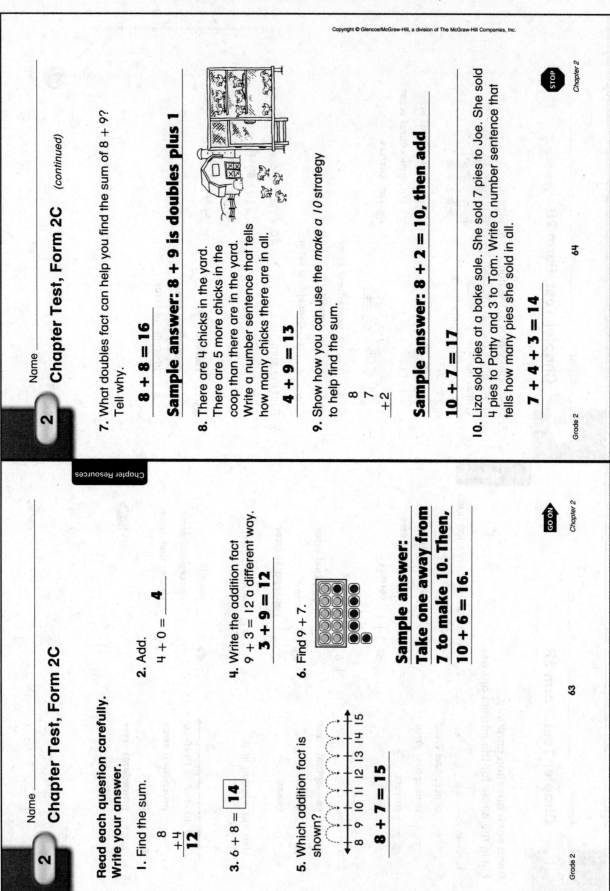

Name _____

2 Chapter Test, Form 2C

**Read each question carefully.
Write your answer.**

1. Find the sum.

    8
   +4
   ——
   12

2. Add.

   4 + 0 = **4**

3. 6 + 8 = **14**

4. Write the addition fact
   9 + 3 = 12 a different way.

   3 + 9 = 12

5. Which addition fact is
   shown?

   8 9 10 11 12 13 14 15

   8 + 7 = 15

6. Find 9 + 7.

   **Sample answer:
   Take one away from
   7 to make 10. Then,
   10 + 6 = 16.**

GO ON   Chapter 2

Grade 2   63

Name _____

2 Chapter Test, Form 2C   *(continued)*

7. What doubles fact can help you find the sum of 8 + 9?
   Tell why.

   8 + 8 = 16

   Sample answer: 8 + 9 is doubles plus 1

8. There are 4 chicks in the yard.
   There are 5 more chicks in the
   coop than there are in the yard.
   Write a number sentence that tells
   how many chicks there are in all.

   4 + 9 = 13

9. Show how you can use the *make a 10* strategy
   to help find the sum.

    8
    7
   +2
   ——

   Sample answer: 8 + 2 = 10, then add

   10 + 7 = 17

10. Liza sold pies at a bake sale. She sold 7 pies to Joe. She sold
    4 pies to Patty and 3 to Tom. Write a number sentence that
    tells how many pies she sold in all.

    7 + 4 + 3 = 14

STOP   Chapter 2

Grade 2   64

Chapter Resources

Name _____

2

Chapter Test, Form 2D

Read each question carefully.
Write your answer.

1. Add.

$$\begin{array}{r} 9 \\ +5 \\ \hline \mathbf{14} \end{array}$$

2. Find the sum.

$$\begin{array}{r} 8 \\ +0 \\ \hline \mathbf{8} \end{array}$$

3. Add.

$$\begin{array}{r} 6 \\ +4 \\ \hline \mathbf{10} \end{array}$$

4. Show another way to write this same fact.

$9 + 3 = 12$

$$\mathbf{3 + 9 = 12}$$

5. Use the number line. Find $6 + 7$.

5 6 7 8 9 10 11 12 13 14 15

$6 + 7 = \underline{\mathbf{13}}$

6. Find $8 + 4$.

$8 + 4 = \underline{\mathbf{12}}$

GO ON

Name _____

2

Chapter Test, Form 2D *(continued)*

7. Add.

$8 + 9 = \underline{\mathbf{17}}$

8. There are 5 horses in the field. There are 3 more horses in the barn than there are in the field. How many horses in all?

$5 + 8 = \underline{\mathbf{13}}$ horses

9. Find the sum.

$$\begin{array}{r} 8 \\ 3 \\ +2 \\ \hline \mathbf{13} \end{array}$$

10. Leo buys 4 melons and 8 ears of corn at the farmer's market. He buys 1 melon and 3 peppers from the grocery store and 2 melons from a fruit stand. How many melons does he buy in all?

$\underline{\mathbf{7}}$ melons

STOP

Chapter Resources

Answers

Answers (Cumulative Test Practice Chapters 1–2)

Name _____

2 Cumulative Test Practice Chapters 1-2

Read each question carefully.
Fill in the circle for the correct answer.

1. How many tens and ones are shown?

- ◯ 6 ones 3 tens **procedural error**
- ◯ 63 ones **conceptual error**
- ◯ 63 tens **conceptual error**
- ● 6 tens 3 ones **correct**

2. What is the value of the 7 in 78?

- ◯ 7 **conceptual error**
- ● 70 **correct**
- ◯ 78 **guess**
- ◯ 80 **procedural error**

3. Find the sum. 6 + 7 = ☐

- ◯ 12 **procedural error**
- ● 13 **correct**
- ◯ 14 **procedural error**
- ◯ 67 **guess**

4. Add. 8 + 2 = ☐

- ◯ 2 **guess**
- ◯ 4 **guess**
- ◯ 6 **conceptual error**
- ● 10 **correct**

5. 9 + 7 = ☐

- ◯ 10 **procedural error**
- ◯ 11 **guess**
- ● 16 **correct**
- ◯ 17 **procedural error**

GO ON

Name _____

2 Cumulative Test Practice (continued)

Read each question carefully.
Write your answer on the line.

6. Vera bought 6 ears of corn. Sal bought 2 ears of corn. How many ears of corn do they have now?

8 ears of corn

7. There are 10 cherries in the bowl. About how many cherries would it take to fill the bowl?

50 cherries

8. Kayla plants three kinds of peppers. She plants 3 red peppers, 7 green peppers, and 5 hot peppers. Write a number sentence that tells how many peppers she plants in all.

$3 + 7 + 5 = 15$ **peppers**

9. Derrick buys 6 apples. Edgar buys 2 fewer apples than Derrick. How many total apples did they buy?

10 apples

10. Mimi uses her calculator to add 3 to numbers. She adds in this order: $2 + 3 = 5$, $3 + 3 = 6$, $4 + 3 = 7$, and $5 + 3 = 8$. If she continues the pattern, what will be the next number sentence? $6 + 3 = 9$

STOP

Chapter Resources